The Immobile Man

▲ A neurologist's casebook ▲

Meeting Challenges

CHALLENGING EVENTS in our lives shape our futures. They may take the form of psychological dramas or social pressures or physical illness, and they can be genetically or environmentally induced.

The practice of medicine involves helping patients meet these challenges both by identifying the diseases that affect them and mastering the treatments, and also by giving comfort and understanding where no treatment is possible.

I am moved and amazed by the way my patients face trials that can change the course of their lives—right to the end. The stories in this book are about ordinary and extraordinary people. Some deserve to be given a medal for their heroism—others don't know how to earn one.

The
Immobile
Man

▲ **A neurologist's casebook** ▲

Lud Gutmann MD

Mc Clain Printing Company
212 Main Street
Parsons, West Virginia 26287
2008

Some of the stories in this book
have appeared in the following publications:

Neurology: "Finding the Answer," 2005;65:969-971
"Limelight," 2008;71:297-298
"The Prosecutor," 2006;66:1282-1283
"The Tattoo," 2005;65:177-178
"Never Saw it Coming," 2005;65:1993-1994
"Flat Tire," 2006;66:778-780
"The Coal Miner," 2006;67:1720-1722

Moment: "The Old Man from Freiburg," 2004(June);35-37

Goldenseal: "Doing it Right on Ambler Ridge," 2005(Spring);47-51
Some have been edited and all are reproduced here
with permission from the publications.

International Standard Book Number: 0-87012-781-0
Library of Congress Catalog Card Number: 2008940477
Printed in the United States of America
Copyright © 2008 Lud Gutmann MD
1117 University Ave., Suite 302
Morgantown, WV 26505

MY PATIENTS are the inspiration for this book.

A NEUROLOGIST'S CASEBOOK
TABLE OF CONTENTS

NOTES ON THE STORIES

A MEDICAL STUDENT and I were looking at a series of MRI images on the computer screen. They showed the inside of a patient's skull—the detailed anatomy of the brain displayed in high relief. The student pointed at a large oval-shaped mass lying between the skull and the right temporal lobe.

"There, isn't that a cyst pressing on the brain?"

I said, "Yes, but how long has it been there and is it the problem?"

The referring doctor thought it might be the cause of her intense headaches and wanted a second opinion. Talking to the teenager, we learned that the headaches had the characteristics of migraines and were associated with her mother having the same headaches when she was young. The stresses of being a college freshman contributed to our patient's recent worsening pain. I thought the cyst that showed in the scan was a benign collection of fluid, present since birth, and of no real importance. I later uncovered a scan from years before that showed the same cyst and confirmed my opinion.

It was the girl's description of her headaches that led to the correct diagnosis and subsequent medical treatment. The scan gave an answer—there was a cyst outside the brain—that could have led to useless surgery for a benign mass that was not related to the headaches.

In spite of the development of new technologies and tests that see inside the body, learning about the patient's life remains crucial in medical analysis. After a lifetime in medicine, I still put the patient's story first before going to the seemingly easy answers given by mechanical means.

The science of neurology is based on complex interactions—some may be physical, some emotional. It is easy for the physician to be seduced into relying on sophisticated imaging and laboratory studies alone when seeking an answer to a patient's problem. Collecting detailed information about the patient as a unique individual is equally as important as probing the scientific and biological facts.

Careful questioning about life experiences, family relationships, passions, nightmares, and emotional strengths and weaknesses reveal the person behind the illness. Each patient's story has a unique outcome: one may pose an ethical dilemma, another, a transformative experience, many have poignant conclusions—through it all, the whole patient must be understood in order for the physician to find the answer. These stories are chronicles of understanding.

The Immobile Man

THE OLD MAN sat as if carved into his ancient wooden wheelchair. For the first fifteen minutes I watched him he never moved a muscle except for the slow involuntary tremor of his hands. He never blinked—just stared straight ahead—his face, an expressionless apathetic mask.

I was told that in the past two years he had walked only with great difficulty. His speech was no more than an indistinct and incomprehensible mutter. I was a third year medical student working with patients for the first time. I never learned his name or anything about him, he was just an anonymous person in the late stage of Parkinson's disease. Whatever thoughts, hopes, and dreams he may have had, no one taking care of him ever knew. They said he had no visitors.

As I watched, the nurse in charge of his care, for inexplicable reasons, began tormenting and berating him. She called him lazy, yet she knew he could understand her even though he could not respond. She finally turned her back and began to move away. Whatever cruel instinct prompted her pointless diatribe, no one could foresee his response. Without warning his face became bright red, the skin of his scalp stretched tight, his fringe of short white hair stood erect and he suddenly unfroze—a statue unexpectedly coming to life. He arose from his chair like a wounded beast, and, amazingly energized, ran after his tormentor and raised his cane—ready to smite her onto the floor of the hospital ward. Just as he was on the verge of striking he suddenly froze in his tracks, his feet glued to the floor, his raised arm assuming a grotesque pose. He would have fallen but for a student nurse who helped him into a chair.

What hidden memories had this unfeeling nurse stimulated? What were the recollections, sufficiently powerful, to ignite this astonishing moment of action and reprisal?

We marveled at an explosive event that seemed medically impossible. We should have been just as curious and amazed at the hidden emotions that had been unleashed.

Finding the Answer

THE AMBULANCE slipped quietly down twenty blocks of upper Broadway past the entrance to the George Washington Bridge. This was not the Great White Way of midtown Manhattan, with its brightly lit animated billboards, theaters, and tacky movie houses. Here—on the northern tip of Manhattan Island—the street was lined with gray, nondescript apartment buildings, kosher butcher shops, bodegas, Chinese laundries and other 1950-style small stores. It was already dark, the evening dreary and overcast. The ambulance moved silently, stopping at an occasional red light. No screaming siren or flashing lights—on purpose.

"The lights, the noise, it makes people crazy," the driver said, turning to me in the next seat. "They crash into things. Besides," he continued, looking back at the old man lying on the gurney, "he looks like he'll make it to the Neurological Institute just fine." This driver seemed to know what he was talking about. He was a calm, old, experienced hand and I wasn't calm or old or experienced—in fact, I was young and terribly upset.

It had all begun earlier in the evening. I was a third year medical student assigned to the general medicine wards at Columbia Presbyterian Hospital and had just returned home to Bard Hall, the student dorm on Haven Avenue. The note I found in my mailbox read, "Urgent. Please call Mrs. Katz, your uncle's housekeeper. He had a stroke." I called her right away.

Uncle Sidney was my favorite relative. Most of the older family members called him Friedl, short for Siegfried, but he'd Americanized his name when he immigrated to New York. Sidney lived five blocks from the hospital. I'd seen him just two days before, as I did nearly every weekend.

"Ludwig," Mrs. Katz said on the phone, her heavily accented voice trembling with urgency, "I found your uncle unconscious this afternoon when I came up to clean. I called the doctor who said he had a stroke. He sent your uncle to the hospital. I think you better go see him." She gave me the address. I'd never heard of it. It was up at 193rd Street.

"Poor Sidney," I thought. Life had been difficult for him. He'd been injured in World War I but he never talked about it. Between the wars he'd been a successful milliner in Europe. I remembered he had an elegant shop in Mainz but dearly loved his visits to the fashion centers in Paris. It was an era when women's hats, veils, and artificial flower pins were the height of fashion. He barely escaped from Germany before World War II, moving to New York with his wife, Cecily, and her spinster sister, Emily. Cecily died shortly after their arrival and Emily a decade later. He was fond of both women and their loss was devastating to him.

The early evening traffic on Broadway was light and the cabdriver moved swiftly up the 25 short blocks. The buildings were just a blur as I urged him to drive faster.

"Hey, Doc," my short white jacket, with my new stethoscope poking out of the pocket, had been a dead giveaway, "just sit back and relax. I'm going as fast as I can."

We almost missed the apartment building that was supposed to be the hospital.

"Hold it," I practically shouted as our cab drove past it. "I think I see a sign saying Jewish Memorial Hospital."

It looked like any of the other dull, grimy brick structures in upper Manhattan. The small off-white sign with black painted letters was posted high up, next to the entrance door.

"Good luck, Doc," the cabbie said as I rushed through the main door of the building. The entry was dark and dingy; the only light coming through the glass front door. The antiseptic smell of Clorox was overpowering. One wall was lined with mailboxes with the elevator and stairs opposite. Another sign posted next to the elevator said, "Jewish Memorial Hospital, 3rd Floor," apparently the building was an apartment house from the ground floor to the third—an unusual arrangement.

The stairway was dark and narrow, the marble steps well worn by years of use. On the third floor the stairwell opened on a gray hallway. A pudgy tired-looking woman in a white uniform sat at a scarred wooden desk. A small plaque facing me announced her name, Mildred Klein.

"I'm Mr. Kane's nephew," I said, breathlessly after running up the three steep flights. "He's supposed to be a patient here. How's he doing?"

"I can't tell you anything except that the doctor said he had a stroke," she answered, not looking up from the book she was reading. "The doctor was supposed to be in earlier but he didn't get here. Probably won't see him now till tomorrow. Mr. Kane's down the hall to the right."

Down the hall to the right was a room dimly lit by only a single, bare 60-watt bulb in the ceiling and divided into four cubicles by white, flyspecked plywood dividers. The floor was covered with red and black linoleum squares. Looking over the dividers, I could see that three of the beds were empty. Uncle Sidney lay on his back in the fourth. He wore only a hospital gown, a clean white sheet neatly covering his legs. His face was ashen in the pale light and he seemed like a corpse except for the slight movement of his chest. Only the soft hissing of the oxygen coming out of a nasal cannula broke the silence of the room.

"Uncle Sidney," I said loudly, "How are you? It's Lud."

No response.

I said it again, louder, and shook his arm.

No response.

I stood there a minute. I felt lost and overwhelmed. How had his doctor arrived at the diagnosis of stroke? He was certainly in coma but there were so many possible causes, I couldn't sort them out. All I could focus on was that something terrible had happened to Sidney and no one was doing anything. And I didn't know how much time I had—was this an emergency?

What a difference from the medicine wards at Presbyterian Hospital—residents were always there to care for our patients and the students helped them. I decided not to call Sidney's family doctor. His antiquated European concepts of health care had originated in another era and were not in keeping with the principles and therapies I was learning. I felt draped with the responsibility to make decisions all alone, and I was ill prepared. I knew I had to do what I always did when I needed help and advice.

"I'll be back," I said, momentarily forgetting that Sidney couldn't hear me.

"May I use your phone?" I asked the nurse who was still reading her book.

"There's a pay phone over there," she pointed to the battered black metal box on the wall near the elevator without looking at me.

Five minutes later, the operator at the Neurological Institute had connected me with the neurology resident on call. All I got was his first name, David. I introduced myself and told him everything I knew about Sidney. "It looks like he's seriously ill and nothing seems to be happening. What shall I do?"

"Do you want to transfer him down here?"

"Absolutely," I answered without hesitation.

"Good," he said, "I'll send an ambulance up there to bring the two of you down. Make sure he doesn't have any problem breathing."

The ambulance driver and I carefully moved Sidney to the gurney. Sidney was limp and loose, like a rag doll without a single bone in its body. He remained completely unresponsive to everything that was happening. The nurse had finally stopped reading her book. As we rolled the gurney onto the elevator she just quietly shook her head.

As we moved along in the ambulance I pictured the past weekend hoping to find a clue as to what might be wrong. It was all about trying to find the right answer. Sidney was an itinerant salesman who catered to the millinery trade. He worked long hours, traveling to shops all over New Jersey and then packing the orders for shipping in the spare bedroom of his apartment. He worried about business, about being alone, and about making ends meet. Being a salesman lacked the security of having a fashionable shop catering to an affluent clientele. Telling funny stories and jokes was his way of drawing attention away from his more serious side.

I went to visit each Sunday and helping him out was my way to pay for the oasis of great food and good company Sidney offered. It was my only respite from the long hours of a medical student in an unfriendly city.

That Sunday I'd helped Sidney pack artificial flowers, hats and veils for his customers before he cooked dinner for us. A bottle of green Chartreuse sat on the kitchen table. Sidney relished the sweet liqueur before dinner. He was a short, stocky man with a large, square, bald head. Two tortuous arteries, like a pair of wriggling snakes, coursed across his temples. He worked deftly at the stove, mixing bits of beef, vegetables, and potatoes into a white enameled pot. I always marveled at the facility he had with his right hand even though the last three fingers were missing—shot off as a young man during the First World War. The lobster bisque, my favorite soup, was already simmering.

This night Sidney was much more serious than usual. "I'm exhausted," he told me. "I'm having so much trouble sleeping. My mind just won't stop—it just keeps whirling around." The Chartreuse seemed to cheer him up. I knew we hadn't packed as many items as usual for his customers. I knew he was worried about business and that he was probably depressed.

David Goldblatt, the neurology resident who had helped me over the phone, was waiting for us at the ambulance receiving area when we arrived. He was a tall, lean man with black wavy hair. He was dressed nearly all in white—neatly starched white shirt, white trousers and white jacket—only his thin striped blue tie added color to his hospital uniform. He stood there quietly as the driver and an orderly maneuvered the gurney from the ambulance.

Sidney was moved to a bright room on one of the upper floors of the Neurological Institute. He was still unresponsive but breathing quietly as David and I reviewed his history. Sidney was 60, had hypertension, but was otherwise healthy. He had mild depressions in the past and recently was having insomnia. He had lived alone for years since Cecily and Emily died. When I was in high school, he often stayed overnight on our farm on Wednesday evenings after visiting shops in the nearby towns. There were times when my mother, his younger sister, didn't enjoy his visits. He was not always a considerate guest. He tormented my schedule-driven mother, as brothers will, by often showing up late and still expecting dinner. Even now he continued his visits to the farm and, I was sure, still showing up late. For me, though, he was a great host.

"Did he have any dizziness or stroke-like symptoms?" David wanted to know.

"He never told me if he did and I'm pretty sure he's never had a stroke in the past," I answered. "All he ever complained about was his difficulty with insomnia. He said he was seeing his doctor about it."

"Did he take any medications?"

"As far as I know, just something for his blood pressure."

David spent the next ten minutes examining Sidney. "He responds a little to pain but that's all," David said, turning to me. "There are no focal findings—nothing to suggest he may have had a stroke. He doesn't move much to pain but he moves all his extremities equally. His reflexes are symmetrical and he has no Babinski signs. There's no papilledema or neck stiffness. I suppose he could have a meningitis or encephalitis—I'll get a skull x-ray and do a spinal tap and get some blood work."

There was no talk about MRI or CT scans. This was 1957 and these hadn't even been imagined. David looked serious, his brow wrinkled, "What I worry about is a drug overdose. Was he taking anything to help him sleep?"

I didn't know.

"Would you mind going over to his apartment and see what you can find as far as other medicines are concerned?" David asked.

Would I mind? My overpowering concern for Sidney and my feelings of lonely desperation over the past few hours were being quickly transformed into an intense sense of excitement. Things were happening—x-rays, a spinal tap, and David was sending me on a fact-finding mission. I was suddenly a participant in Sidney's diagnostic workup. It was as if I was Watson and Holmes had just announced that the game was afoot.

I ran the five blocks to Sidney's apartment. A few lonely souls on Ft. Washington Avenue turned to stare at me sprinting down the sidewalk. I took the stairs up to his apartment two steps at a time. It was an old-fashioned city apartment with small rooms each separated by glass doors. I unlocked the front door—he'd given me a key some years earlier—and saw the double doors to his bedroom were wide open.

The bed sheets were in utter disarray. They were rumpled and half off the bed. The blanket lay rolled up on the floor. The small shaded lamp on his bed stand softly illuminated the entire room, concentrating on the top of the stand. Next to his open gold pocket watch was an open glass pill bottle, its black cap lying inches away. The yellow light of the lamp seemed like a spotlight focused on the pill bottle.

I picked it up. The bottle was only half full with capsules containing a white powder. The label read, "Nembutal." Sidney was supposed to take one at bedtime as needed, the printed directions said. I looked down and saw a lone capsule lying on the floor at the edge of the bed. I had seen enough. Bottle in hand, I ran back to the Neurological Institute.

David greeted my evidence with a quiet smile. "They're doing the x-ray right now. The spinal fluid looks normal and there are no white cells present. He has no infection of the brain. The rest of the tests on the fluid will be done tomorrow but I don't expect anything to come from them. I think the answer is in your hand."

He was quiet for a moment and then added, "That's one of the problems with the barbiturates. Take a couple and they can create a twilight zone in which the patient thinks he is still awake when, in fact, he is sleeping on and off but keeps taking extra capsules."

"Will he be all right?" I asked.

"I think so," David answered. It was late and I must have looked exhausted. "Why don't you go home and get some sleep. I'll watch out over him, I'm here all night. I doubt the skull x-ray will tell us anything. If we're right, he'll wake up tomorrow and feel fine."

The next morning, early ward rounds seemed to drag on indeterminately. It wasn't 'til noon that I was able to break away. Sidney was sitting on the edge of his bed shaving the stubble of the last few days. He looked up and smiled. He looked relieved to see me.

"Nice to have you back with us," I said. I tried to suppress a grin of pure joy.

"What happened?" Sidney asked. "How did I get here? What's going on?"

I told him about the events of the previous day. "I don't know how that could happen," he said, perplexed, "I had trouble falling asleep and I knew I had to get up early for work. I took two sleeping pills. I can't remember taking any more."

I told him about the automatic behavior that can occur with barbiturates and added, "You need to be more careful with sleeping pills."

He nodded his head. "I guess you were right all along. I should have an internist here at Columbia. If you arrange it, I'll see him."

Late that afternoon we walked to his home together. Ft. Washington Avenue was busy with people leaving work or heading over to Broadway for their late day shopping. I'd missed not seeing David Goldblatt but I was sure that, like Sherlock Holmes, he was off finding the answer to the next challenge.

Sidney was full of energy and seemed happier than I'd seen him in months. He had dodged a major bullet and knew it. It had been a brisk fall day, bright and sunny, but a cool breeze was beginning to come off the Hudson River. Behind us, in the distance, the George Washington Bridge was filled with busy traffic heading back to New Jersey. The sun was beginning to set behind the Palisades.

Siggy

SIGGY'S SMALL DELI was shoehorned into the first floor of a grimy tenement half a block off 168th Street. It was a couple of minutes from the tall gray buildings of Columbia-Presbyterian Medical Center in New York City and a popular hangout for medical students. The rusted fire escape that hung high above the entrance looked like an ancient long forgotten thunderbolt calling attention to Siggy's eatery.

A wooden counter and stools ran along one side of the shop while the other had several small tables and chairs. Siggy was a permanent fixture behind the counter, standing in front of a series of shelves loaded with provisions: breads and bagels in their bins, jars of pickles and olives, bottles of juices and pop, cans of tuna and soup, and boxes of cereals. A large refrigerator was always packed with meats, eggs, containers of milk, lettuce, and cheeses.

At breakfast, Siggy was busy frying eggs and bacon on his ever-hot grill, passing out bowls of cereal and milk, and joking around with his medical students in their regulation white jackets, who were eager to finish eating quickly and head to class. Later he grilled hot dogs and hamburgers and made sandwiches for lunch. The smell of frying onions and garlic would saturate the air. The atmosphere was usually hectic, students rushing in and out, laughing, telling stories about their latest encounters with patients or with intimidating professors. Siggy was part of the frenzy. Sarah, his ever-present wife, stoically worked the cash register and added a bit of calm to the otherwise frantic environment.

At quiet times, Siggy liked to lean on the counter and listen to the students telling tales. He was a short, stubby, middle-aged man. His huge hands moved deftly, slicing meats, onions, and cheeses. His head was large. He had a prominent brow and a big jaw. His facial features were coarse with thick lips, a bulbous nose, and thick, oily skin. He walked with a limp that he attributed to arthritis in one of his hips but, despite our urgings, he wouldn't take the time to see a doctor.

"You know," he would tell us, "you boys are so smart, you should figure out a cure for my headaches. I got 'em all the time."

"You ought to see someone at the Neurologic Institute. It's just down the block," we'd say. "We'll even help arrange an appointment."

His answer was always the same, "No, no, I don't have time. I'm too busy taking care of you guys. I'll just keep taking my aspirin."

During my last year in medical school, some of my assigned rotations took me to other hospitals in the city and I didn't see Siggy for several months. On my return to Washington Heights, I dropped in with one of my friends and found Sarah working the grill and Siggy's daughter in charge of the cash register.

"Where's Sig?" I asked.

"He's over at the Neurologic Institute. They took out his brain tumor last week."

"Brain tumor?" I asked incredulously. "Sig had a brain tumor?"

"Yeah, his headaches just kept getting worse and for the last month his eyesight was going. He even got diabetes. I finally made him go see a doctor. They said the tumor was in some gland underneath his brain. They found it on a skull x-ray. The surgery went pretty good. They think he might out in a few more weeks."

I was stunned. I felt like Dr. Watson being admonished by Sherlock Holmes, "You see but you do not observe."

All the pieces suddenly fell into place, it all seemed so obvious. Siggy's headaches, his large head and jaw, his big nose, his coarse oily skin, his huge hands, even his diabetes—Siggy had the classic signs of acromegaly caused by a tumor of his pituitary gland, a tumor that was putting out too much growth hormone.

His headaches were caused by this tumor slowly eroding the saddle-shaped depression in the sphenoid bone at the base of the skull—the sella turcica meaning Turkish saddle. The enlarging tumor was also causing his loss of vision. The enlarging pituitary gland had not only been gnawing into its surrounding bony cavity but had also expanded upward, rising slowly like a baking cake, and compressed the adjacent optic nerves. He had the classic textbook symptoms and body characteristics of this endocrine disorder.

Siggy's acromegaly had evolved right in front of us. We had seen it slowly develop over a number of years, but none of us had put the pieces of the puzzle together. Hundreds of students had been in and out of his luncheonette. We'd even commented on his facial features, but none had made the connection. Why hadn't we? How could we let it all sneak up on us? Was it because he was behind a counter and not in an examination room? Did he seem somehow indestructible—he was such a hard worker, always there, always active? It was difficult to believe he could have had anything wrong with him. In the final analysis, I think we took it all for granted, thinking this was just Siggy.

Siggy's travail happened a half century ago but the events remain vividly displayed in my mind. It has been a constant worry that I would miss a diagnosis as it evolved before my eyes—like missing the wild spring flowers until, suddenly, they are in bloom.

Limelight

FRANK FORSTER SAT behind the desk in his office, his head down, concentrating on the letters he was signing. His dark brown leather chair matched the grandness of the mahogany desk—in both quality and scale they were right for him. The aroma from the smoldering tobacco in his pipe filled the room. On the wall behind him, a framed autographed portrait of President Eisenhower dominated the office. Frank had provided consultation when the President had a small stroke while in the White House and he took pride in the association.

Frank cut an imposing figure. He was tall and generously-sized, always flawlessly dressed with shining shoes and black hair meticulously combed. His closely cropped moustache framed a warm, amiable smile.

He looked up as I knocked lightly on his open door. I was the senior ward resident and he had called me.

"Lud, I need your help," he said. "At two o'clock today I have to present a patient to the first-year medical students as part of their neuroanatomy course. They need to know that what they are learning about the brain has some practical applications so we need someone with some interesting physical findings. Do we have a patient on the wards you think might be instructive for them to see, someone who would be willing to come?"

I thought about it for a moment. We had fifteen patients at the time, but none with anything unusual. "We may have a problem finding a patient," I said. Frank leaned back in his chair and reached for his still smoldering pipe. He lit it afresh and took two long puffs. I felt uneasy and anxious by my inability to identify a patient. Frank smiled, his equanimity undisturbed.

"Let's go over each of one of them," Frank suggested. "Tell me their stories."

I described each patient to him briefly and, when I finished, he said, "You're right. There isn't much to show. Are you sure you haven't forgotten anyone?"

He took another puff and smoke slowly cast a thin cloud over Eisenhower's face. I began to realize that Frank would manage a solution. I remembered rounds earlier in the week when he examined a patient with epilepsy. Sitting on the exam table, the patient had a brief partial seizure. He became unresponsive, stared straight ahead and fumbled with a shirt button.

We saw a patient having a momentary seizure but Frank saw more. "Look," he exclaimed excitedly, "The patient was completely out of contact with us but not with his environment. He remained seated. He didn't fall. He was sufficiently aware of his surroundings that he maintained his position on the table and knew where to find his shirt button." Frank could always see deeply into a situation.

I went over my list more carefully. "Actually," I answered, "we do have one more patient. She's thirty five and has severe cerebral palsy. She's been here for two weeks and she's badly depressed. I'm afraid we've not been much help to her."

"Tell me," Frank said.

"Well, she's lived all her life in a little town in northern Wisconsin and her family has always looked after her. She can't use her arms because they're spastic and uncoordinated and it's hard to understand her because her speech is thick and slurred. This the first time she's ever been away from home. For the last two weeks she's just been lying around crying. Physical and occupational therapy haven't done a thing."

"Poor lady," Frank said, "no wonder she's depressed. She must be a total invalid without useful arms. She couldn't possibly do anything for herself. Eating, dressing, going to the bathroom must be impossible."

"No, Not really," I said. "She does a lot for herself. She uses her feet. She's actually pretty good with them."

Frank suddenly sat up, bristling with excitement. He was out of his chair, reaching for his white coat. "Let's visit her," he exclaimed, hurrying out the door with me rushing to keep up with him.

Margaret was lying quietly in bed, staring at the ceiling as she did most of the time. Her straight, mousy brown hair was cut short, as if someone had put a bowl over her head and chopped away at it. She was wearing no makeup and her arms lay awkwardly at her side. I introduced Frank to her and he sat down next to her bed. He told her that he'd heard what a hard life she'd had and how brave she was and how she could do all kinds of things with her feet. He gave her his broad, engaging smile. "Would you show me?" he asked.

Frank seemed to awaken something in her. She nodded and reached for her comb with her right foot. Grasping it deftly, she combed her hair. "I can feed myself, too," she said, pronouncing the words slowly and with great difficulty. He was genuinely impressed and Margaret could see his delight.

He took her useless hand in his. "Margaret," he said, "my young medical students need to understand from the beginning that patients can do surprising things on their own behalf. You could help me show them how a remarkable woman can take care of herself by doing things in a different way. They need to see the way patients can rise to a challenge. Will you come?" She seemed pleased with the request and nodded her head, yes.

At two o'clock I wheeled her into the big amphitheater. The nurses had dressed her in pretty flowered pajamas and placed two red ribbons in her neatly combed hair. She sat propped up on pillows on the gurney, her comb and brush and lipstick lying neatly next to her right foot. Frank was already there, talking to the 120 students in the rows of seats rising up from the amphitheater floor. As soon as he saw Margaret, he turned his full attention to her. He stood beside her, his arm around her shoulders, beaming down at her. "Thank you so much for coming," he said.

Then, his arm still around her shoulders, he turned to the students. He told them about this brave woman from a town of a hundred people in northern Wisconsin. He told them about how she had been born at home, with the umbilical cord wrapped around her neck, about how blue she had been, and how hard the country doctor had worked to keep her alive.

"She's never had much schooling and she could never use her arms, but she learned how to help care for herself, using her feet," he announced. Turning to Margaret, he asked, "Can you show them?" And Margaret did. She combed her hair, then brushed it and applied her lipstick skillfully.

"I understand you can feed yourself using your feet," Frank said to her. That was my cue. I walked over and placed a bowl of red strawberry jello and a spoon at the foot of the gurney. She grasped the spoon handle with her toes and then, deftly, used the spoon to eat the Jell-O, not spilling a single little jiggling cube. Frank beamed and thanked her. Almost on cue, all 120 students rose from their seats and clapped enthusiastically.

Now Margaret was beaming too, while I was trying to keep from crying. There were tears in the audience, as well. Later, when we transferred her from the gurney to her bed, Margaret was still smiling.

The next morning on rounds, she was sitting up in bed waiting for us. For the first time in weeks she greeted us. The happy smile I had seen the day before was still there. In her slow, thick speech, pausing between each word, she said, "I feel so much better. I want to go home. You taught me that I really am somebody after all, that I have done something with my life—that I do matter."

The Prosecutor

SAM WALKED SLOWLY toward the autopsy suite. It was hidden away at the quiet end of the ground floor of the medical school building. He barely noticed the histology technician, carrying a tray of slides, coming toward him. He was preoccupied, immersed in the problem that a county prosecutor from one of West Virginia's southern counties had presented to him earlier that morning. He opened the door automatically and allowed it to close softly behind him as he entered the brightly lit room.

"Our funeral director called me two nights ago to come over and see something," the prosecutor had said to Sam over the phone. "So I went over there. He sounded real upset. And I could see why. They got this body of a nine-year-old. I mean we live in a small town and nobody's hardly ever seen this kid. And there she is in the funeral home—nine years old and weighing 35 pounds. She looks like she's right out of some concentration camp. She don't have no bruises but I think this is a straightforward neglect and abuse case."

There was more to the story. The prosecutor had talked with some of the neighbors. They said the mother was withdrawn and kept pretty much to herself. She was young, unmarried, and lived on welfare and food stamps. When the mother did occasionally come out over the years, the neighbors said the child seemed very small and undernourished. They never saw her walking but always lying on a red cart the mother pulled. No one ever saw the little girl talk or even cry. She never went to school and was never seen at any social events. The mother hadn't been seen in church since the baby was born.

"I think I'll file criminal charges against the mother after I get your report," the prosecutor added. "Right now I need to know if there's been any brain injury. Of course, I have to know the cause of death."

Sam was the first neuropathologist at West Virginia University's new four-year medical school. He had already made his scientific reputation at the University of Wisconsin and had come to Morgantown to be part of a fledgling clinical neurosciences team.

Sam was a soft-spoken man with a seemingly placid, round face and jet-black hair. His constantly somber expression portrayed the seriousness with which he took his responsibilities. He looked older than his 38 years.

As Sam walked into the autopsy suite, he got his first look at the small, pale body lying in the middle of the large, black dissecting table. The round operating room light was focused on the little person and Sam approached her with a sense of gravity. Here was this tiny child, now devoid of all her spontaneity, her movements, her interactions with those around her, a mere shell of the real person—like a tree in the midst of winter, stripped of all its vibrant blooms and leaves.

Sam held his breath for a moment as he looked at her well-formed body and head. Her face was thin, her body gaunt, and her straight, blond hair pulled back in a ponytail. The morgue technician, a tall, lean man wearing a green gown and cone-shaped mask, had cut a long incision extending across the child's scalp from one ear to the other and pulled back the edges to expose the skull.

Sam watched patiently as the room filled with the high-pitched whirring sound of the power saw. The technician held the small saw deftly as its circular blade cut into the thick bone. When he finished, he carefully lifted up the top half of the skull exposing the glistening dura mater that hid and protected the brain lying beneath it. He stepped back, placed the saw on a metal cabinet next to his other instruments, and nodded to Sam.

Sam had put on a green gown that hung loosely from his broad shoulders, almost touching the tile floor. As he walked to the table, he pulled on a pair of skin-colored latex gloves. Then he picked up a scalpel lying next to the child's head and deftly incised the dura and skillfully cut away a few fine blood vessels that connected it to the skull. With two swift strokes of the scalpel, he separated the brain stem from the spinal cord deep in the cranial vault. Grasping the brain lightly with both hands, he lifted it out and placed it carefully on a bright metal tray to one side of the child's head.

He paused for a moment, looking at the brain as it now sat neatly on the tray—it was clearly unusually small. Carefully pulling back the dura, he gave a short silent gasp of surprise. The usual gyri—the in- and out-foldings of the brain hemispheres so characteristic of the normal human brain—were missing entirely. Instead, the surface of the brain was unwrinkled and perfectly smooth, as if tightly encased in stretched shiny silk. Sam had seen this rare malformation of the brain—a genetically determined defect of neural migration called lissencephaly—before.

Sam didn't have to wait two weeks for the brain to be fixed by formaldehyde; he already knew there would be a marked loss of cells. The child had been born with a seriously malformed brain. She must have been severely retarded.

The observations from the neighbors reported by the prosecutor were those that Sam would have expected in a patient with lissencephaly. What was so unusual was that the child had lived to be nine. As Sam sat in his office a short time later, looking through his books and files, he learned that death invariably occurred by two years of age in all other cases reported in the medical literature.

Sam finally called the mother. She was taken aback by his call. "I really don't know if I should be talking to you," she said, "People think I've been a bad mother and I'm kinda' scared. They say I'm probably going to jail." She sounded frightened.

Sam tried to be reassuring. Speaking softly, he told her, "I've just examined your daughter. She was born with a very abnormal brain and that's not your fault. I promise you I'm going to write a good report but I'd appreciate knowing more about her from you."

"Well, OK," she answered slowly. The relief in her voice, even over the phone, was obvious. "I've really done my best to be a good mom but it's been so hard. She never acted like other babies. She never moved much, never sat up, would eat almost nothing. I was so ashamed, I kept her inside the house most of the time. I was afraid people would say bad things about me. They did, anyway, me with no husband and all. Once in a while I'd take her for a ride in her red wagon – she seemed to like that. Toward the end she just stopped eating. I loved her so much, she was my whole life—I'm really going to miss her." Sam could hear her crying softly.

"I'm sure you did take great care of her," he said. "In fact, I know you did and, from what I've seen, I think it must have been exceptional. You've been a wonderful mom."

When Sam finished the autopsy and had all the facts together, he placed two phone calls—one to the prosecutor and one to the mother—and gave them both all his findings and his interpretation. Instead of the child having been abused and neglected, her long survival (actually the longest ever reported for a child born with this malformation) spoke to the devoted care she had received all through her nine years' of life. On hearing all this, the mother cried in gratitude, glad that the doctors at the big university had appreciated her efforts.

"Oh, thank you," she said. "You know, I have a picture of her. If you like, I'll send it to you."

The picture came a week later. The child was lying in the red wagon, wearing a pretty blue dress decorated with colorful embroidered flowers. Her hair was pulled straight back and tied with a brilliant ribbon. It was the kind of picture that would be taken by a proud and loving parent.

The prosecutor said he was pleased to close the case. Sam put the picture on his office wall.

Woman in Motion

THE DISHEVELED WOMAN sitting on the exam table had the appearance of an imaginary creature from a science fiction comic book. Her hair was stingy and uncombed, her fingernails dirty—in fact, she was grimy all over and smelled as if she hadn't bathed in days. Her loose fitting jeans and baggy T-shirt gave a flailing quality to the uncontrolled jerking of her arms and legs. The fronts of her tennis shoes were frayed as if gnawed open by the constant movement of her toes.

Her furious glare presaged her opening sally. "Look, I don't want to be here. They," she said, looking angrily at the older couple sitting silently off to one side, "made me come. They think you're going to help me but I doubt it."

The older woman wore a plain house dress and was as thin as her daughter. Her hair had streaks of gray, her eyes had the resigned look of a parent carrying a never-ending burden. The man, clad in jeans and a work shirt, silently watched the young woman restlessly moving about on the table.

The young woman, Holly, looked morosely at me. "Everyone knows I don't sit still very well. I have these tics and I can't stop them. I've had 'em for years. I don't know why."

She looked like she had a permanent case of the fidgets. The quick involuntary jerks of her arms, legs, and trunk and her sudden, uncoordinated bows seemed like caricatures, not real

gestures, they were so frequent. Holly tried to hide the movements by pretending she needed to scratch her face or rub her
head, but these twitches were impossible to disguise and they
looked like chorea to me. "Chorea," is from the Latin word for
dance—and an uncomfortable dance it was for this poor young
woman.

I asked her to squeeze two of my fingers with her hand and
it felt as if she was milking my fingers; this is so typical of
chorea it has a name of its own—the "milkmaid's sign." The
exam was otherwise normal except for her sullen disinterest
and poor knowledge of current events.

There aren't too many causes of chorea in a young woman.
The obvious conclusion for a neurologist is Huntington's disease, but one of her parents should have been similarly affected, and neither was. I'd been scrutinizing them as closely as I
had Holly. They sat quietly and in control, watching their
daughter and me. There was not a flicker of movement between
the two of them.

I thought about other possibilities so I questioned both
Holly and her parents. "We have to look into all the likely causes. Rheumatic fever in childhood and pregnancy both can have
symptoms like yours." They adamantly insisted neither was the
case, and when I asked her about drugs to prevent pregnancy,
another rare reason, she sneered at me and said, "Those are for
sissies."

Her mother spoke up. "I'm sorry she's behaving so bad.
She was never like this before. She was never real smart, but
she was always a good girl. The last few years she's been running around with a motorcycle gang, drinking beer and smoking marihuana. She cusses all the time and just tears up the
house if we say anything. Me and my husband don't know
what's going to happen next."

Everything pointed to Huntington's disease, but one of the parents should also have been afflicted. They weren't, and that was the problem, since this is a dominantly inherited disease. They had married before Holly was born and neither knew of anyone in their families with such an illness.

It was time for some tests. I had other patients to see. I said I'd meet with the family again in the afternoon and sent them to the lab. Holly wasn't happy, but decided to go along with the plan. "I'm ready for lunch. I'm hungry all the time, so if we can go eat after the tests, I'll stay for a while. I got nuthin' else to do, anyway," she said as she marched out of the exam room. I sensed that her bravado masked a very real fear. She was trying to cover the symptoms, so it was clear she knew her body was out of her control. Teenagers are hypersensitive to body changes; they have just been through profound ones in growing up. Her strange, ungovernable twitches must have been noticed and talked about by her friends. And she was not hanging around with a kindly, sympathetic crowd. Friends like the ones she had can be cruel.

The tests came back in the afternoon. The pregnancy and test of the thyroid, and the heart echocardiogram (looking for the heart valve changes seen in rheumatic fever), were normal. No surprises here. The DNA test for Huntington's disease and the copper studies for Wilson's disease would not be back for weeks. However, the MRI scan of her brain showed mild atrophy of the caudate nucleus, a collection of neurons that shows shrinkage in Huntington's disease.

I remembered a description I'd read from a talk given by Dr. George Huntington. Huntington first described this unique disease in 1872, unpublicized until then. His father and grandfather, both doctors, had kept notes on a set of patients who had a unique familial chorea. Over seventy-eight years of study, they documented and studied the disease as it kept on appearing in East Hampton, Long Island, New York and nowhere else in the world that was known.

Huntington wrote, "Riding with my father on his professional rounds, I saw my first case of 'that disorder' which was the way in which the natives always referred to the dreaded disease....Driving through a wooded road...we suddenly came upon two women, mother and daughter, both tall, thin, almost cadaverous, both bowing, twisting, grimacing. I stared in wonderment, almost in fear. What could it mean? From this point on, my interest in the disease has never wholly ceased."

Subsequently, Huntington added the observation that, "The hereditary chorea...is confined to...a few families and has been transmitted to them, an heirloom from generations away back in the dim past...hardly ever manifesting itself until adult or middle life, and then coming on gradually but surely, increasing by degrees, and often occupying years in its development, until the hapless sufferer is but a quivering wreck of his former self. When either or both parents have shown manifestations of the disease...one or more of the offspring almost invariably suffer from the disease, if they live to adult age. But if by any chance these children go through life without it, the thread is broken and the grandchildren and great-grandchildren of the original shakers may rest assured that they are free from the disease.... I have never known a recovery or even an amelioration of symptoms in this form of chorea; when once it begins it clings to the bitter end."

More than a century later, this all remains the same, except it is not confined to Huntington, Long Island, but has spread to the entire world. In fact, today there are thousands of people with the illness.

The most famous person with this illness was Woody Guthrie, the American folk singer, who died in 1967. I often wondered why it wasn't called Woody Guthrie's disease—the way amyotrophic lateral sclerosis, an equally devastating neurological disease, is known as Lou Gehrig's disease. I supposed baseball players get more attention than balladeers. Then, again, maybe George Huntington had the early claim.

Dr. Huntington's observations were very much in my mind when, in the afternoon, I met Holly and her parents again in the clinic. I was convinced she had the disease. Everything led to that conclusion—her chorea, her antisocial personality, my examination, and the MRI changes. I told them my conclusions, but said we would have to wait two weeks for the DNA results. Holly smirked. "DNA's not gonna' make any difference. That's for criminals. I told you there was nothing wrong with me. Let's get out of here." She looked ready to flee.

I didn't want to wait for the DNA test, either. I felt a need to know, to plan some help for the girl in this desperate situation. But I had to be very wary and tactful and try another approach. "Can I have just a few more minutes? Won't take long." I asked Holly's mother to come to another exam room with me to take a test.

As we walked out, Holly yelled, "Don't take long or I'll be gone!"

We walked slowly to another room. I shut the door and asked her to sit down facing me. "You know," I said softly, "I really think Holly has Huntington's disease. The DNA will prove it one way or the other, but I don't want to wait weeks for the test results. We need to get her started on some medication right now to help with the way she's acting. But I need to be sure I'm right and I'm still bothered that there's no family history of the illness. And, to be sure, I need to ask you a very serious question." She sat very still, hardly breathing, waiting.

"Are you sure your husband is Holly's father?" It was only a moment before she began sobbing quietly, then reached out and gripped my hand.

"I was afraid it would finally come out," she answered between sobs. "My husband doesn't know he's not Holly's father. When I was sixteen I got raped by this horrible man who had all the same jerking of his body that Holly has. He'd just gotten out of the state hospital. He was awful. I was desperate and didn't know what to do. I was going with my husband and I decided to get married sooner."

"I'm really sorry," I said. I squeezed her hand. I had just let the evil genie out of the lamp.

I knew she was overwhelmed by the thought of telling Holly and her husband. There was little in the way of effective treatment for the disease, but I could prescribe something for Holly's psychiatric symptoms and, perhaps, some counseling when and if she was willing. It was difficult enough to deal with this miserably unhappy young woman without having her hear her mother's dreadful story. At this point the expensive DNA test was superfluous.

Holly's mother was still clutching my hand. I could feel her fear and wanted to reassure her. "Don't worry," I said, "You don't have to tell her history to anyone except me. I had to know the truth. It can be our secret. You can tell anyone who asks that the disease could have been caused by a spontaneous gene mutation. As I said before, this has been known to happen, although rarely.

"Next, we need to get Holly some help in living with Huntington's as it slowly worsens. We do have medicines that can decrease some of her abnormal movements and calm her down. It won't stop the slow, relentless progression of the illness but it will help her function more productively and make it easier for you to live with her. We'll try to buy some more good time."

I thought, how terrible for a mother to find she has unwittingly and helplessly passed on such a curse to her offspring, but besides feeling for the mother, it was also an important ethical issue for me. Who owned the information? The mother, certainly, but what about her husband and Holly? Holly's mom had confided this devastating story to me alone and I knew I had an obligation to her to keep her secret. I remembered the Hippocratic oath and its emphasis on doctor-patient confidentiality. There was really no need for the mother or me to tell her family, since nothing would be gained medically. Some situations are better left open and unconcluded—I left it to her to decide what to do about telling her husband at some time in the future.

But what about Holly? As is the case with so many genetic illnesses, there are no effective treatments available. Her uncontrolled movements and personality disorder would only worsen relentlessly. Medications would be of little benefit, alleviating some of the anguish and turmoil but not the underlying brain deterioration. The prognosis remains unchanged from Huntington's description over one hundred years ago.

Obsession

Obsession is the single most wasteful human activity, because with an obsession you keep coming back and back to the same question and never get an answer.

— Norman Mailer, quoted in an interview with Divina Infusino
from *American Way*, June 15, 1995

BOBBY CALLED and said he and his wife, Jane, would like to drop in to my office. It had been a busy morning but I cleared my calendar so we'd have time to talk in the afternoon. I was glad to see them both. They had been students at West Virginia University twenty-five years earlier, she a college undergraduate and he a medical student, and I remembered them well.

Jane sat quietly for while as Bobby and I talked about the past. He had been a child of the 1970s with his carefully combed pony tail held neatly in place with a light blue rubber band. He rebelled against wearing the prescribed dress shirt, neck tie, and neat trousers. Instead, he came to the clinic wearing carefully pressed polo shirts and jeans. In place of shoes he wore expensive colorful wool socks and sandals. When seeing patients, he was especially adept at organizing the details of their symptoms and exam findings into a coherent picture and arriving at a correct diagnosis. I was disappointed when he chose radiology instead of neurology as a specialty.

We had not seen each other for years and I was glad to catch up with their lives. Bobby's practice had been successful and, even though he and Jane were both only in their late fifties, they were planning to retire shortly to Myrtle Beach. I was pleased they had stopped in to renew their old acquaintance with me.

They both looked too young to retire, especially Jane. Still slim and beautiful, she had aged well. Her blond hair and gold rings were highlighted by a dark brown tan. Professionally applied makeup largely hid the wrinkles that plastic surgery had failed to eradicate, wrinkles etched by years of sitting in the sun and lying on tanning beds. She wore a tight black dress that emphasized her shapely figure. It was easy to visualize the popular college cheerleader she had been. Bobby told me that she had helped manage his practice, since they had no children.

As Bobby talked, growing more and more animated, I wondered when Jane would join in—it was her turn to enter the conversation. Bobby seemed to sense this, too, yet rather than slow down he seemed to talk faster. Finally when he ran out of steam and paused, I turned to Jane. "Now it's your turn to fill me in. Are you looking forward to retirement? No one will believe you're of an age to retire, that's for sure."

Jane leaned forward in her chair and, with no lead-in or preliminary talk, looked directly at me and quietly stated, "I think I am dying of ALS."

It fell like a bombshell. No one spoke. I looked back at her, and saw she was deadly serious. I finally repeated, "ALS? Lou Gehrig's disease? Are you sure? Where did that diagnosis come from? Would you like me to provide you with a second opinion?" Bobby's head was down. He was making no eye contact with either of us.

She didn't answer immediately and I waited, giving her time to collect herself even though she didn't seem upset. But she had to be. She was living with a tragic burden, looking down the gun barrel of life and seeing her death.

"I haven't actually seen anybody about my symptoms," she finally said in a very even tone. "You're the first doctor I've talked to about them—except for Bobby, of course. He says you're the expert, so here I am. I've read all about the disease and there is no question that I have it."

For a moment I was overwhelmed by the tragic news as any friend would be. Then, slowly, I moved back into my objective neurologist mode and began to look at Jane more critically and analytically. Over the years I had seen many patients with ominous diagnoses which, on careful reassessment turned out not to be the case. I would start from the beginning and see where the facts led me.

I hoped Jane was wrong. ALS was the most dreaded illness in my practice. It was a relentless disease in which the motor neurons of the brain and spinal cord slowly degenerated along with the muscle fibers that these cells innervated. This was an untreatable disease from which there was a never a reprieve. Death was inevitable—usually in three to five years—and was invariably due to the muscles needed for breathing and keeping the airway clear being too weak to sustain life.

What had started out as a pleasant social afternoon had suddenly turned serious—a bright, sunny day quickly becoming overcast. I began questioning Jane closely about her symptoms.

Jane was aware that she had some muscle twitches, known as fasciculations, which may accompany the muscle weakness and wasting of ALS. This seemed to be the reason she felt she had the disease. Over the course of the afternoon I examined her carefully, even doing a sensitive electrical test—an electromyogram—that can identify early motor nerve fiber and muscle degeneration. Except for a very few muscle twitches, I couldn't find anything abnormal. I was relieved to see that she had no muscle weakness and atrophy or abnormal reflexes— the hallmarks of ALS.

When the test results were in, I sat down and spoke directly to Jane. "I know you're worried about the small muscle twitches you've been having, and I think that's why you picked out ALS as the culprit, so you'll be glad to hear my really good news. At this time I can't find anything to suggest that you have ALS. It's true that fasciculations are almost always a part of the disease, but they are most often benign, especially when there is no muscle weakness or atrophy and when the electromyogram is normal."

Bobby was clearly pleased and relieved, but Jane was skeptical. Her voice had an edge when she asked, "How can you be so sure? Is your exam so conclusive that you can say that with 100 percent certainty?"

"Jane," I answered, "I'm never 100 percent sure of anything, but I really don't think you have ALS. Even though the disease is uncommon, there are only forty new patients each year in West Virginia; in this hospital we end up seeing most of them. So even though ALS is rare in the general population, we have a lot of experience and we think we're pretty good at making the diagnosis."

Jane still looked skeptical, so I decided to make sure she knew what she was suggesting. As a doctor's wife, managing his practice, she had ample access to research, but maybe she'd confused the name. So I gave her a little lecture—full description, no holds barred.

"Jane, lets go over the details of this disease, so we know we're both talking about the same thing. ALS is short for amyotrophic lateral sclerosis and it is devastating." We talked about the slow progressive degeneration of the motor cells and nerve fibers that supply the muscles along with a relentless, progressive loss of muscle power and muscle wasting in the arms, legs, and chest wall. Speaking, swallowing, and breathing would become impaired, while mental faculties remain intact. "There was no effective cure in the 1930s," I added, "when Lou Gehrig died of the disease, and there isn't any now."

Jane nodded her head as I talked. She had read all about it. She had been sure of her own diagnosis and she didn't want to let it go. I could see she expected more from me—her diagnosis to be taken seriously, perhaps, or she, herself to be taken seriously, who knew? So, after a moment, I said, "Why don't I see you again in three months and we'll do the whole evaluation all over?" Both she and Bobby thought it was a good idea and we left it at that. I wondered if Jane really had understood my description to her of the symptoms and findings of ALS and the relentless progression of the disease. She certainly didn't credit my examination—her faith in her own opinion remained strong.

Three months later, on schedule, I met Jane and Bobby in the examining room. "I'm worse," Jane announced immediately. "I feel weak all the time. I'm even more sure I have ALS." Bobby looked at her with an expression of concern but with some confusion. She had worn little makeup and was casually dressed. She did look tired and not her usual pulled-together self.

Again I examined her carefully and again I found no muscle weakness or wasting—just a few fasciculations here and there. Strangely, I felt almost apologetic when I said, "I still can't find anything." I went on to explain again. "In ALS, the muscles are weak. They don't have their normal strength.

Patients may also describe weakness when, in fact, they are simply fatigued or have little energy, like a runner at the end of a race who is tired but whose muscles are really still strong. Maybe you're just tired." She shook her head. Then I decided to venture a new idea, "Do you think you're a little depressed or stressed?"

"That's not the answer," she replied in an exasperated tone. "Bobby's good to me, we have two houses, a Porsche and a Mercedes, and plenty of money. If I'm under any stress, it's caused by this awful disease I know I'm slowly dying from."

I could see that Bobby wanted to end the conversation. He got up and quickly suggested I see her again in three months, so we scheduled the next visit. As they left, Bobby was solicitous toward Jane, maybe too solicitous. I began to sense an element of frustration and annoyance.

He called me the next day from his office. I was glad he did. "You're pretty confident she doesn't have ALS?" he asked.

"Yes I am," I answered. "It's true that ALS is invariably associated with fasciculations, but the fact that she doesn't have the more telling features of the disease after more than six months is very convincing to me. I don't understand her obsession with ALS and dying. She tells me there are no stresses in her life except her non-existent disease. It's hard to believe. I mean, we all have stresses in our lives. When we're together, I can't get her to talk about herself at all. For Jane, there's only one topic."

"You're right," Bobby said. "Except for discussing minute details of her symptoms, she has little to say. She's always been a very private person. We talk a bit about friends and money and what's going on in our world but never about our feelings. Now we don't even have small talk. Sometimes I think our marriage is just a convenient arrangement."

"It wasn't always that way, was it?"

"I not sure as I think about it now. Those years in college and med school were hard for me. I was really trying to find myself and I was pretty angry. All the long talks you and I had back then really helped me. She and I never had a conversation about anything like that—even during the time leading up to the marriage and certainly not after."

I remembered it all well. Bobby, a skinny little med student with his ponytail and sandals seemed to be rebelling against something, but we never talked about that. Our exclusive subject was the future—Bobby's future, to be exact, but that was typical of student-professor conversations. And I liked to chat with students in this way, especially with Bobby. He worked hard and was bright despite all his personal turmoil. The long discussions, and the sense that I was helping Bobby find himself, had made him one of my all-time memorable students. I was disturbed to find his successful life was now so full of personal difficulty and I was worried.

"Jane was a gorgeous cheer leader and the sex was really great for me," Bobby said, thoughtfully. "That was her big attraction, I'm afraid. I wasn't really interested in her as a person—I never got to know her that way. And for her, I think she liked dating a med student and the idea of being a doctor's wife was important to her. It certainly was to her mom and dad. That really scored points with them. You know we got married just after graduation and before I went on to become a radiologist. There was a reason for the early marriage, of course. She thought she was pregnant. It didn't turn out to be true and I've always wondered if it was a concocted story. She swore I was wrong, but we never had children and it wasn't because I had a problem. Her parents were pleased when she married me. They didn't know the reason."

"Why do you think it was so important for them?"

"Well, you have to understand them. Her dad was an insurance salesman and money was always a big issue for him. Fancy cars, a big house, nice suits, staying at expensive hotels—that's what it was all about. He worked really hard and wasn't home a lot when she was growing up. At the same time, she never lived up to his expectations. She was never smart enough, never good enough, never quite pretty enough, and he let her know that constantly. Positive feedback was not part of his approach to his daughter. Her mom ran a beauty shop and looking good was a virtue for her too. Both of them were very demanding of Jane, and very strict. Jane used to tell me how her mother controlled her diet when she was growing up—they noticed if she gained even a few pounds. As Jane got older, they looked over every boy carefully before they allowed her to go out on a date. None of her boy-friends ever lived up to their expectations and they made no secret of it."

"Do you think they loved her as she was growing up?"

"I suppose, in their way, but I've never really been sure. If they did, they made her work for it. I think they always resented her, especially early on. They didn't want any kids and, when she came along, it didn't set too well. Like I said, she always had trouble pleasing them. No matter how hard she tried, it was never quite good enough. By the time she got to junior high, the pressure on her was to be the best looking, the best dressed, the most popular, the best cheerleader, and eventually marry someone who'd make a lot of money. I have to say, she really tried to meet their expectations and to satisfy them. She also worked hard running my practice and making it a financial success. I worry that closing it down—taking away a major purpose in her life—and moving to Myrtle Beach is part of her problem now. That, and the fact that she's starting to lose her good looks."

The next visits produced the same test results and we had the same conversation. Each time Jane announced that she was more and more confident that she had the disease and was getting worse. I, in turn, continued to find nothing to support her conviction. She finally decided to get a second opinion from one of my colleagues at the Mayo Clinic, where she got the same answer. Bobby said she was really annoyed with this specialist. She accused him of calling me for my opinion (we had been together as residents at Mayo) and depending on my diagnosis and not thinking for himself, and on and on. It must have been a very uncomfortable scene. Of course, he hadn't called me at all, but she wouldn't believe either him or me.

Well over a year had passed and there were still no findings to support ALS. I was as close to being 100 percent certain as I could be. Her situation was totally static. I was disturbed by her obsession that she was dying of this terrible disease. I tried again to persuade her to see a psychiatrist. It was very disappointing when she refused, but there was really no more I could do. Bobby remained quiet during the visit. I had the feeling he was getting annoyed at her persistence, but he kept his feelings well hidden and took her arm to assist her as they went out. She wore no make-up at all now. Her blond hair was shot through with gray and, this time, as for both of the previous examinations, she was dressed in a casual outfit in an unbecoming pastel color with no jewelry except for her wedding band—the opposite of her former stylish self.

Some months later, I heard from a well-known neurologist in Washington, DC—we were old friends from medical school but now rarely saw each other. "I'm calling because I'm seeing your patient, Jane, and I'd like to discuss her case with you," he began. "Tell me about her. She claims she has ALS and that she's seen you recently. Is that what you think she has?"

I told him the whole story, including my conclusion—that this was a belief for which I could find no basis in fact. "I assume you're seeing her for yet another opinion?" I asked. "She's been up to the Mayo Clinic and they told her the same thing. She was nasty to them. ALS has become a real obsession with her."

"No, I'm not seeing her for another opinion, although I'm sure you're right. Actually, I'm not seeing her in my practice. I was asked to do a special consultation by the South Carolina prison authorities."

There was a long pause while I took in this information. I remembered that one of Jon's academic interests was looking for brain abnormalities in criminals. He had recently published an article about his research in the *New Yorker* magazine.

"I don't understand. A prison? What happened?"

"This is quite a story and I'll tell it to you as best I can put it together from the information I got from her and from the prison officials," he said.

"After she and her husband saw you on their last visit, they decided to spend some time at their new home in Myrtle Beach. There, over the next several weeks, Jane's fixation on ALS became stronger than ever. She demanded that Bobby take her to Johns Hopkins and she says he refused. 'I pleaded with him to let me go but he said no,' she told me she had said. He blew up—told her that nothing had shown up in a year and a half and he believed the two experts she'd already seen were right—that she didn't have ALS, that it was all her imagination, and that she needed psychiatric help. This discussion probably happened late in the evening. Bobby then went to bed. Some time after he fell asleep, Jane shot him six times with a pistol."

"Jane what?"

"Jane shot him six times with a pistol. And there's more. Jane then wasn't sure whether to shoot herself or not. She decided not to, but waited seven days before calling 911."

"Seven days? She waited seven days?"

The coroner's report suggests that Bobby may have survived the shooting for twenty-four hours before he died. The prison authorities asked me to see her because this was such an unusual case."

I asked him to wait. Then I set the phone aside and put my head down on the desk for a minute. All I could think was; poor Bobby, all Jane's suppressed anger welling up and overflowing like an erupting volcano. If only I could have gotten her into treatment. I didn't see the violence coming.

When I found my voice again, I asked, "How is Jane doing? Is she depressed? Remorseful? What will happen to her?"

"It's my opinion that no jury will ever recommend the death penalty," he answered. "She seems hardly to think about Bobby, though. It's as if he never existed. Her major concern is that she is dying of ALS and that everyone's missed it."

It was like a Greek tragedy. On thinking it over, I wondered who it was that Jane thought she was shooting—Bobby or her father. I heard later that the case never went to trial. Jane admitted she had killed her husband and was sentenced to twenty-five years in prison.

Secret History

"Are you married?" It's a routine question I ask everyone as part of taking their history. This patient was a forty-year- old woman who had come to me for help because of a curious set of neurological symptoms that seemed to have no basis in any disorder of the nervous system.

"No, I'm a widow. My husband passed away."

"What did he die of?" I asked, almost as an afterthought.

She paused, then answered in a matter-of-fact and seemingly unemotional tone, "I shot him. He was an abusive man—just like my father had been—and the court said it was justifiable homicide."

I thought, "Poor lady. Now that is a burden."

IT HAD BEEN a long day and I was tired. I was seeing my last hospital consultation —a twenty-five-year-old woman whose body had been paralyzed on the right side for several days.

Jeremy, a new neurology resident, had seen Tina earlier in the day and recounted the details of her history and findings in the corridor, outside her room. Before we entered, he added, punctuated by an expression of puzzled concern, "She looks like she's had a major stroke, but there are some worrisome things that don't add up." He ticked them off as he spoke, "She has almost none of the risk factors for stroke—no high blood pressure, no diabetes, no high cholesterol, and no heart dis-ease—except she smokes two packs of cigarettes a day. Also there are no problems with language, none of the aphasia or slurred speech one might expect from a stroke that produced right-sided paralysis, and her reflexes are the same on both sides. Finally, her MRI scan is flat-out normal. It didn't show a tumor, a stroke, or anything else abnormal. I don't think it's a physical problem. My guess is she's faking it."

Based on the information Jeremy had given me, I shared his concern that what appeared to be a stroke, might not be. A stroke in the brain is due to blockage of an artery supplying blood to parts of the brain. The blockage is usually caused by a blood clot in an area of arteriosclerosis. When the artery is a large one, such as the middle cerebral artery, a large portion of the brain under-goes degeneration—the medical term for damaged brain tissue is infarction—and a number of symptoms occur. If the infarction is in the left side of the brain—the dominant side—the language and sensory areas and the visual pathways are often destroyed in addition to those controlling motor function. The patient will have difficulty expressing herself or understanding others and be unable to see in the right field of vision. There is usually weak-ness on the right side which will be associated with an increase in reflexes and loss of sensation on the right side of the body.

On the other hand, the blockage may involve only a tiny artery causing a tiny infarct—a lacunar infarct. The lacunar infarct may be as small as the head of a pin but, if it is in an important area, such as in the motor pathway, it can cause weakness on one side.

The more I thought about it, the more I thought that Jeremy's concerns were right on target. With only weakness of one side, I supposed she might have a small lacunar infarct but her age made even that unusual.

I knocked on the door and we went in. Tina was lying comfortably (too comfortably, perhaps) in bed watching television. She looked like a carefully manicured Barbie doll, with light blond hair streaming onto her shoulders, crimson lipstick carefully applied, a pale blue nightgown cut low, and, in the cleavage between her breasts, a tiny gold chain with a heart-shaped locket.

We three were alone; there were no family members in the room. I pulled a chair up next to her bed, glad this was the last patient and I could sit down, and balanced the open chart on my knee. I told her I was a neurologist and asked her a series of questions to verify and amplify the resident's report, beginning with, "I understand you're paralyzed on one side. How did it happen?"

"I woke up in the morning a few days ago and discovered I couldn't move my right side. It's pretty numb too." She spoke in a flat, quiet voice.

"Has it gotten any better? Can you move your right side at all?"

"Don't think so."

"Did anything unusual happen the night before?"

"Not really. Me and my girlfriend went out for a movie and a couple of beers. My husband was kinda mad 'cause I wasn't home and didn't have his dinner ready for him and then me coming home late, well..."

"Can you try to move your arm?" I asked. She seemed to try but there was not even a flicker of movement. Yet, when I held her supposedly paralyzed arm above her head and let it drop suddenly straight down, she moved it sideways to avoid hitting her body. She had no weakness of the right side of her face when I asked her to show me her teeth. She said couldn't move her right leg and she told me she couldn't walk.

I was becoming more and more impressed by her lack of concern and total indifference—*"la belle indifference"*—a term coined by the French to describe the languid behavior of a beautiful woman and a perfect description of Tina's passivity. Her quiet, controlled voice and relaxed body seemed unusual for a person suddenly paralyzed—someone who should have been terribly upset.

I suspected that Tina was likely having what is called a "conversion reaction." Her symptoms mimicked a physical condition but were really a response to overwhelming psychological stress. Abuse—whether mental, physical, sexual or a combination of these—is often the basis for the stress. Tina was not faking it, but her automatic reflex of protecting herself by pulling her right arm away when I dropped it couldn't be fooled, so her body reacted normally.

How is it possible that emotional stresses can cause one-sided paralysis or other neurological symptoms? Where are the connections from the mind to the brain? How does the impact of past experiences result in paralysis or cause convulsions that look like epileptic seizures but are driven by earlier emotional trauma?

The brain is an anatomical structure composed of a myriad of neurons all connected by a vast array of nerve fibers. Groups of neurons have specialized functions so that some see or hear while others move parts of our body or feel. Mixed into this network of brain cells are those that serve the functions of what we refer to as the mind. Just as the brain controls our abilities to see, hear, feel and move our body parts, it also has the ability to experience the environment and to think.

The mind is in reality an integral part of the brain and not an actual anatomical structure. The cells and nerve fibers that subserve the functions of the mind are part of the brain. The mind is not just connected to the brain; it is inherent within the brain. Events that affect the mind may influence bodily functions. Anxiety can cause a tremor. A young couple seeing each other may experience increased heartbeats or develop sexual urges. These are examples of mind-body relationships.

The more serious question is, how does a stressful event marshal the complex symptoms of a conversion reaction—a mental disturbance manifesting itself as a physical disorder? Most adults who grow up in a loving and supportive family environment have the personality strength to effectively contend with a hostile or otherwise emotionally distressing situation. It may be upsetting but most of us can deal with it successfully. However, a flawed and traumatic background during childhood results in the personality defects that make managing this difficult. Depending on the nature of the stress, a patient may use primitive defenses as shields. A conversion reaction represents one of these defense mechanisms.

I was about ask more personal questions to find out the cause when I suddenly had the eerie feeling that someone was watching. I turned around quickly and saw the door of the room slightly ajar. A man was peering through the crack, but as soon as he saw me look, he shut the door and was gone.

I turned back to her. "Do you and your husband get along? You told me he got angry with you the night before your stroke."

She hesitated, "I guess he's okay most of the time, but he can get pretty mad at me if I don't do what he wants—especially if he's drinking." She seemed unconcerned; her voice was still flat.

"Does he just get mad or does he beat you sometimes too?"

"Yeah, sometimes he beats me pretty good, but mostly when he's drunk." She answered in a matter-of-fact-tone, as if these things happened every day.

I persisted, "Did anyone else, other than your husband, ever beat you or molest you? Other boyfriends? Your father?"

"My father never molested me but he did beat me. He left us when I was seven or eight. My mom got herself a boyfriend then and…" She paused. Her mouth tightened into a tense, thin line as she remembered. I waited, hoping she would continue, hoping she would admit it to herself and not close down the opening wedge into her memory. Finally I said, quietly, encouragingly. "And?"

"And… he would force me to have sex with him when she was at work." She said it quickly, still with no emotion, looking past me at the cabinet in the corner. Her statement had slipped out almost like an unconscious thought, almost as if she had been unaware of saying anything.

I responded immediately so that the moment wouldn't pass. "Did it happen a lot?"

"It did for a few years, but when my mom found out about it she threw him out. No one else ever done it to me."

It was a story I'd heard too many times before. A young woman, abused in the vulnerable years of childhood, marries or lives with an abusive man when she becomes an adult. A cruel and violent man ought to repel her but, more often than not, the opposite occurs—like a hostage attracted to her captor.

Suddenly the door flew open and the man who had been peering in earlier burst into the room. The patient and I had been speaking softly so I didn't think he had heard any of the conversation. I had a quick impression of a big, burly man in bleached blue jeans. His chest seemed ready to burst through the stretched cotton of his tight, white short-sleeved T-shirt. A pack of cigarettes was stuck into his rolled-up left sleeve over muscle-builder biceps and his fingers had a characteristic tan stain. His gray eyes had a menacing look and his mouth was twisted into a snarl. I stood up quickly. I glimpsed Jeremy backing into a corner of the room, his face pale and startled.

"Are you the guy who told my wife earlier today that she was crazy and that's why she's paralyzed?" He was screaming—enraged. His neck grew red and mottled and the flush spread up into his face. He was starting to sweat. "I'm going to show you what I think of that kind of crap." He grabbed my shirt and tie at my neck and began shaking me.

He had his fist drawn back and I was preparing to duck when his wife said, in the same quiet, toneless voice she had used all along, "Lay off the Doc, Sam, it wasn't him that told me that stuff."

Sam loosened his grip and I grabbed my instruments and retreated to the safety of the nursing station. Jeremy was close behind. Sam didn't follow us and I could see through the open door that he wasn't menacing Tina. I quickly jotted my notes in the chart and I suggested that the nurses call security to come and stand by, just in case.

Jeremy and I moved across the hall to the doctors' work area and closed the door. It was time to talk. "You were, of course, right about our paralyzed lady," I said, "She hasn't had a stroke. But what did you mean by faking it? Were you implying it was conscious or unconscious?"

"I hadn't thought about it," he answered.

"I usually limit faking to the patients who do it consciously," I said. "That's very uncommon. Those patients usually have obvious secondary gain—like trying to get a large insurance settlement. And there's the Munchausen syndrome—named after the tall-tale-telling German Baron—where the patient fabricates symptoms to get medical attention. Most patients have a conversion reaction and reflect their inability to handle the stresses in their lives in a constructive fashion. They are often women who've been abused as children."

He had that guilty look I had seen so often in young residents when they'd missed a crucial part of the story. "Who told her she was crazy?" I asked.

"Not me," Jeremy responded. "I just told her that a lot of things didn't fit with her having a stroke and I thought she needed to see a psychiatrist."

I put both my hands on Jeremy's shoulders to get his full attention and looked him dead in the eyes, trying at the same time, unsuccessfully, to suppress a smile laced with both humor and a sense of frustration, "You know," I said almost in a whisper, "when you get to the bottom line too fast, and especially when there is a highly charged emotional problem present, events have a way of going out of control." I thought of the times I'd been guilty of doing the same thing—times when I had been too focused on the problem and the solution to the problem and too busy to take the extra time.

One way to quickly deal with the problem is to plead ignorance. "I can't find a cause for your weakness and I'll report the results of my exam to your doctor." I have seen other physicians use that approach but that always seemed like I would be abrogating my responsibility.

These situations are like time bombs. Somebody is ready to blow up at a moment's notice. If it's not the patient, it's the volatile spouse. You have to be much softer, more gentle, and very, very careful and tactful.

Can she handle the information you are trying to have her understand or is it so threatening that she rejects it? Is she ready to explore this murky area of her life or is physical therapy the best we can offer her?

Conversion reactions aren't so difficult to diagnose when you've seen the pattern again and again. The history of abuse, especially sexual, is a common fellow traveler. It's treating the patient that's hard. Even if the patient makes the connection, addressing it is tough and requires the right kind of help to do it—lots of counseling and psychotherapy. That is, if she'll do it at all.

"Connections with the past," I said to Jeremy, "are like heirlooms you wish weren't there. They're important and your job is, first of all, to suspect they may be there, and then to dig them out without having them blow up in your face."

I remembered a favorite fictional radio hero of my boyhood, the Shadow. The introductory line on the show was: 'The weed of crime bears bitter fruit.'

"If all this awful behavior is amazing to you," I said, "it's still amazing to me, too, no matter how many times I've seen it. Years ago, when I was at your stage of training, nobody had any idea that this kind of thing was going on—that fathers and uncles were molesting little girls and boys and even their own daughters. But I'm sure it was. Human nature doesn't change that much and it's probably been going on since Adam and Eve left the garden with their family. It is an awful transgression—one of the worst crimes I can imagine. It haunts the victims and affects them throughout their lives. At least today we're aware of it and can try to help."

EARLY THE NEXT MORNING I went up to the room to see Tina, checking the hall for her irate husband before I went in, and found she had left. The nurses told me the husband had been so infuriated at the suggestion of a psychiatric cause that he had forced her to leave the hospital with him the evening before, right after I left, against medical advice. The nurses were amazed—her paralysis seemed to have suddenly disappeared. "I thought her chart said she was paralyzed on one side, a nurse said, frowning at me. "The night nurses said the patient needed only a little support from the husband to walk out the door. Could the chart have been wrong?"

I stood transfixed for a moment and wondered if I'd made a chink in Tina's armor. We'd lost the first round, certainly. Now would she look for help somewhere else or maybe come back on her own? Not right now, anyway, since she'd gone off to sleep with the enemy again.

The Old Man from Freiburg

I was ambivalent about making my first trip to Germany. I remembered my mother's admonition. She said—without ever a doubt or qualification—that even though German literature, music, and art were wonderful, her holocaust experience taught her that Germans were genetically evil. She said she would never set foot on German soil again. There was I, though, in 1980, making my first trip to Germany at the urging of a good friend, a German doctor.

I had just arrived, driven 60 kilometers to my destination, and was unwinding with a long jog. As I ran past a cemetery, tired and jet-lagged, I had the sudden sensation that storm troopers were hiding behind every gravestone, ready to shoot me. I was glad to escape to the sanctuary of my hotel room.

DIRK WALKED INTO the office where I was working at his desk. I was editing his initial draft of an article about our first research project together. It was a warm spring afternoon and bright sunlight streamed through the large open windows. He leaned over me and peered down at all the corrections and changes I'd made with my red pen and looked amused. "My poor manuscript looks like it has a bad case of measles," he said. "I had no idea that my English was so bad."

"It's certainly a lot better than my German," I said, laughing. "Another few manuscripts and you'll be writing without my help."

"Why don't you put that red plague of yours aside and see a patient with me?" Dirk said. "He's an older gentleman from Freiburg with poorly controlled epilepsy. His neurologist called me last week and thinks he may be a candidate for surgery. Assuming you can tear yourself away from your desecration of our manuscript, that is."

Dirk was a large, muscular man whose kindly, thoughtful, and serious demeanor hid a well-hidden aggressive and competitive side — the side that had made him one of the outstanding professional German soccer players only a decade earlier. He was always neatly dressed: tailored slacks, light blue button-down shirt, and loose-fitting sweater — but he rarely wore a tie. His long brown hair was forever in need of combing. This casual style was typical of the young physicians in Germany. I liked working with him; he was extraordinarily bright and always anxious to share new ideas. Our collaboration would ultimately result in a series of publications.

Dirk's office was in the university clinics, a series of post World War II architecturally unimaginative gray buildings set on a hill near the downtown of Mainz, Germany. I was working with him on a research project and helping him learn how to write for American scientific journals. Dirk was well known in Germany for his expertise in the area of epilepsy and patients from all over the country sought his advice and help.

It was a quiet Friday and we had finished our studies for the day. I had just been marking time working on the manuscript. "Sure," I said, "I'll join you."

The patient and his wife had come by train from Freiburg that morning and were sitting in the examination room when we arrived. He was elderly—I judged him to be around eighty—and sat upright in a chair. He had a rather formal bearing. His hair was all white and he wore it in a short crew cut. He was dressed in an expensive gray suit, white shirt, and blue silk tie. His steel gray eyes and perpetual polite smile seemed to send the message that he was here as part of an official interview.

When we entered, he immediately stood up, shook our hands, and introduced his wife. "My name is Klaus Kramer and this is my wife, Gertrude Kramer," he said. She was a small woman in a neat brown suit and a cream-colored blouse buttoned high at the neck. She wore no make-up and her only jewelry was a small string of expensive pearls. Her hair was straight and parted in the middle of her head. It had been dyed dark brown with a faint tinge of orange. She sat politely, her hands folded, and nodded to us at her introduction.

"My neurologist in Freiburg advised me to see you," the patient said, after we had all sat down. "I have had epilepsy since I suffered a head injury when I was twenty years old. My family doctor calls them grand mal seizures. They have never been really well controlled. I would have one or two every year even though I have always taken my medications just as advised by my doctors. However, for the last few years, they have become more frequent. I have had one every two months even though I am now taking three medications for epilepsy. They tell me that my MRI scan shows a scar in the temporal lobe of my brain and my doctor thinks that removing the scar may stop the seizures."

"Is this the first time you've been to a university epilepsy center?" Dirk asked.

"No," he answered, "I've been to the universities in Wurzburg and Cologne but the neurologists there said they couldn't help me."

Dirk had been listening intently to the story. "How serious was the head injury?" he asked.

"I hit my head on the front windshield during a car accident and was unconscious for a few days," he answered. "The doctors thought I had injured my brain. Fortunately, I recovered completely except for the epileptic seizures. Despite everything, I have been able to successfully manage the family brewery. Our beers are very popular; but the company takes a lot of work — long days, with few vacations. My wife thinks that may be part of my problem."

When he finished, Dirk said, "I want to hear more about your seizures, but I'll begin my examination while you tell us more."

The patient took off his jacket, tie, and shirt. He wore no undershirt and sat stiffly on the exam table wearing only maroon-colored briefs and black socks. Dirk got up to begin the examination and checked the patient's reflexes. Then he seemed to have second thoughts, stopped, and sat down again.

The patient continued telling his story, but Dirk seemed preoccupied and was only half listening. "My wife says the seizures are very severe. I fall and lose consciousness. Then I stiffen and some seconds later I jerk all over. I usually bite my tongue and lose my urine. I always have a warning before each seizure. I think you call it an aura. I see a large brick building with a tall red chimney. I can't tell what it is but I think it is a factory. It is always the same vision before every grand mal seizure."

Yes, I thought, the features of his seizure disorder make him ideal for epilepsy surgery. It was hard to imagine why two other university centers had turned him down. Clearly, the seizures had never been well controlled despite his using three anti-epileptic drugs and that is a major prerequisite to be a surgical candidate. His déjà vu before each convulsion indicated that an abnormal focus — an area of injured brain — from which his seizures arose were likely located in the temporal lobe.

I had taken the MRI films from a large white envelope that leaned against the wall next to his chair, and put them up on the view boxes. I looked at them while he talked. They showed a scar in the right temporal lobe of the brain. Dirk would need to launch into a detailed laboratory evaluation in preparation for the surgery.

I turned from looking at the films and was surprised to see Dirk standing up, looking out the window as the patient, somehow unaware of Dirk's obvious inattention, continued, "I think my having seizures is dangerous to…"

Dirk suddenly interrupted him. I was struck immediately by the change in the tone of his voice. "I'm really not interested in hearing any more about your seizures. In fact, I have no interest in helping you control them. I have other things I need to do. Once you get dressed, you may leave."

The patient arose and formally announced, "Doctor, I apologize for wasting your time. I do understand."

I looked over at his wife, who had been silent during the entire visit. Her eyes were downcast, focused on the floor. As she and her husband left, she made no eye contact with either of us.

Back in Dirk's office, he lit his pipe and took several deep, long puffs. The smoke rose lazily toward the ceiling. He liked smoking but I had never seen him smoke in his office before. I was mystified about the events with the patient. Dirk was a kind, caring, and sensitive physician and his abrupt behavior was completely uncharacteristic. He finally said, "Let's talk about the manuscript you were working on."

I couldn't let it go. "Wait a minute, Dirk," I said, "I think I'm missing something. What happened in that room?"

"Lud," Dirk answered, "he was not a nice man and I don't need to take care of him. Let's forget it."

"I don't understand," I continued. The patient had seemed polite and sincere to me.

"Okay," he replied. "Did you see the tattoo on his arm when he took his shirt off?"

"Yes," I said, "but I couldn't make out what it said."

"Well, I saw it clearly," Dirk responded. "It was his blood type."

"So, what?" I asked.

Dirk gave me his warm smile. "Oh, Lud, you Americans live such a sheltered life. An old German with his blood type tattooed on his arm means only one thing. He's a former SS officer, a Nazi"—Dirk's smile gave way to anger—"and he can go to hell."

My mother would have approved of Dirk's decision. I thought about the criminals—even an occasional murderer— that I'd treated over the years. The Hippocratic Oath doesn't address the ethics of treating villains but should a doctor judge his patients?

The Curmudgeon

"DOCTOR," HOWARD ANNOUNCED firmly, "I've been diagnosed with a neuropathy. No one knows the cause and I've been referred to you for specialized treatment. I have to tell you that I am sick and tired of having to use this damn cane and not being able button my shirt or zip my fly. I want this fixed and I don't care what it takes."

He gripped his cane tightly and tried tapping it on the floor for emphasis as he spoke. It fell clumsily from his hand. He made an annoyed harrumph and didn't reach down for it.

Howard was a large man who must have been muscular in years now long gone. He wore a dark gray suit and looked almost formal except for a light blue checkered sport shirt buttoned at the top. His jowls, his clear blue eyes, his wrinkled pink face, would have given him a soft, cherubic look were it not for his perpetual scowl. Howard was used to giving orders, I could see. It isn't easy to give up authority and feel energy slipping away with age. So I nodded, smiled, and said nothing. His wife, Betty, remained silent too, but seemed unfazed by all his bluster. She reached over and handed him his cane. Howard adjusted his grip as it kept slipping from his hand. "Just look at this," he said. "I can't even hold on to this damn stick."

"Actually, his doctor thinks he should use a walker in the house," his wife said softly.

Howard shrugged his shoulders in irritation, "It's no damn good. I bang it into everything," he said glaring at me. "What's more, I hate using this wheel chair. It's all happened over the last ten weeks—and I tell you, this whole business is rotten." His pink cheeks were turning red.

All his indignation and anger did not change the fact that Howard had a serious problem. His arms and legs were weak and limp, like overcooked spaghetti. Add to that the loss of his reflexes and he had an overwhelming peripheral neuropathy.

Disorders of the peripheral nerves are frequently seen in a neurologist's practice but it is unusual for them to be this severe. Diabetes, alcoholism, kidney failure, and some medications used to treat cancer are common causes. Howard was healthy, however, and had none of these risk factors. The electromyogram— electrical tests of his nerves — gave the answer. He had chronic inflammatory demyelinating polyneuropathy, CIDP for short, a problem in which the fatty insulation, the myelin, of the nerve fibers is damaged but the fibers themselves remain intact. CIDP, like other autoimmune diseases, is caused by the body's immune system misfiring—mistakenly making antibodies directed at its own cells. In this case the attack was on the Schwann cells which lay down the myelin around the nerve fibers.

The nerve fibers, stripped of their myelin insulation, lose their ability to properly transmit electrical signals from the brain to the muscles. Howard had a sufficient number of demyelinated nerve fibers so that many of his muscle fibers were cut off from his brain's control. His weakness was due to these isolated muscle fibers. Howard was right—it was difficult to tolerate.

I explained the diagnosis to my irritable patient and his wife. "There are several medicines we can use that can correct this problem. The outlook should be good," I said.

"Do whatever you want," he said testily, "just fix it." He gave the impression that his time was important and I might just be wasting it. His impatience made me smile to myself even though his attitude was annoying.

"We'll use prednisone and azathioprine," I added. "These are two drugs that will suppress your immune system and give your nerves a chance to heal. The medicines have some possibly serious side effects and I will have to check for that every few months."

"Look," he interrupted, "I can't worry about side effects. I want to be rid of the problem. Just give me the medicines."

I looked at his ninety-year-old wife. "I think I understand what you are saying about side effects," she said. "I'll try to convince him that he needs to take them seriously." Her expression said this might be a problem and she might not be equal to it. I doubted she had ever convinced him of anything.

When I had examined him earlier, I had realized he was forgetful and was having problems remembering recent events. Now I was concerned about his judgment. It was not just that he was disagreeable and bad tempered, he likely had an early dementia—the beginnings of Alzheimer's disease. All this, along with the fact that his wife was just as old as he, complicated the whole idea of carrying out a treatment plan in which the medicines required careful monitoring. I decided to delay beginning the medications for one week. This would give me a chance to contact his sons and see what could be done. "I need some time to work out a treatment program for you," I said, "and we all need to think about a way to get you back at regular intervals to check on possible side effects."

Howard left, his housekeeper pushing the wheel chair. I could hear his annoyed grumbling all the way down the hall.

It was nearing five o'clock, Howard had been my last patient and I was ready for a run. After writing myself a note to call his sons in the morning, I changed and set off on my usual loop along the Monongahela River. Running has always helped me work out the pressures of the day. I thought about Howard and his nasty manner as I made my solitary afternoon trip.

I knew it wasn't personal—it was his frustration with his illness, not with me, that drove his anger. Still, at times I felt overwhelmed by the stresses of encounters with my patients and, at other times, with their families.

Earlier in the month, I'd seen an elderly woman with the identical problem—only it was more severe. Her chest muscles and diaphragm were so weak that breathing was difficult. I had admitted her to the intensive care unit to begin treatment, not just with prednisone and azathioprine, but also plasmapheresis to get a rapid improvement. Before we could begin, her breathing faltered and she needed to be placed on a ventilator. Her daughter immediately demanded I disconnect her. "Momma told me this was never to happen. She is ready for the Lord." All the while the patient was nodding her head in agreement.

My refusal to discontinue the mechanical ventilation was met with the daughter's anger. "You have no right to make that decision," she said, her nostrils flaring. It took an hour of intense discussion including the intercession of their minister and my guarded assurance that she would likely recover before both daughter and patient agreed to continue the ventilator care. Fortunately, I was right and she walked out of the hospital a week later.

Howard's weakness was less critical—ICU care was not an issue—and would likely respond just as well to the medications. It was his nasty personality that would make compliance a problem. I hoped his sons could give me some perspective and help care for their father, but neither had come with their aging parents to the appointment and that might have been a clue. Still, they were my best chance for success.

The next day, I called one of Howard's sons, Mike, and learned that Howard and his wife lived alone in town across from Howard's Motors, a car repair shop he started and ran for forty years. When Howard had turned 70 he sold it to his sons.

"He used to come down regular," Mike told me, "but he was always critical of how we ran the business. He and my brother were always fighting about something."

Both sons lived nearby, but never visited their father if they could help it. They met their mother for lunch once a month and took their parents out for holidays. Howard was better on neutral ground.

The day I first saw Howard and Betty, their current house-keeper had driven them to the clinic. I gathered there had been a succession of housekeepers who didn't last long, and this one might not either. She was reading the newspaper and, I imagined, likely studying the Want Ad section while she waited.

Mike and I discussed the details of Howard's illness and the immunosuppressive drug therapy. "He has to come in regular-ly," I said, "but he doesn't take it seriously and your mother may not be able to coax or persuade him—she certainly can't force him, I can see that.".

"Nobody has ever been able to force him to do anything," Mike said, "What do you suggest?"

"Your parents are both very old. You might consider being more involved in their lives, especially in the management of his health care since he lives near where you work."

"Get more involved?" Mike's voice rose above the back-ground screech of a metal saw, "Wait a minute, dealing with my father is impossible. He's always been bad-tempered—the only reason his customers put up with him for so many years was the extra care he gave their cars. He was a master mechanic, but he's never been as bad as he's been in the last year. Now, he's just an angry curmudgeon. He wants to be totally independent and he's made that clear to us. Mom goes along with him. I know it doesn't make any sense at their age, but no one tells my father what to do, especially his two kids. At least he doesn't come to the shop and tell us what to do anymore. We go back and forth on the back road to the garage so we don't meet him."

Parents and their children—the roles do reverse sometimes. I remembered an elderly friend who said, "My kids are taking over my life…" with rueful, helpless sorrow, even though he knew it was necessary.

I wasn't willing to give up, "You and your brother need to convince your parents that at their age some help from the family is a good thing. His dementia, even though it's early, makes it harder for him to control his anger."

Mike exploded, "You don't understand!" he said, almost shouting. "My brother can't spend five minutes with our father without getting into an argument with him. My father has always been an abusive man and my brother always got both barrels. I learned long ago to avoid my father's wrath by staying off to one side, but neither one of us wants to stand up to him or—and I know this sounds mean—to do anything for him, either. He knows it all. After all these years, we're still afraid of him."

I understood how he felt, but I didn't want to deny his father the treatment that was available, and the only way I could see Howard getting help was with the cooperation of his family—whom he had clearly alienated through the years. No easy answers here; the son was the only hope.

I decided to try a different approach: perhaps Mike could imagine himself in his father's shoes. "I suppose I can justify not treating your father," I said slowly, as if I were thinking about it carefully. "If your mother can't care for him, there's always a nursing home." I let the last phrase hang in the air.

After a very long pause, Mike sighed and said, "Even though we're pretty busy at the garage, I can always find time to break away. I suppose I could help out. If Dad is willing, I'll bring him to his appointments with you and anybody else he needs to see. Maybe he'll agree but I doubt he'll like my taking him. He'll see it as interference. I think my mother will help supervise his taking the medicines correctly if I help her. Maybe we can set up a system with his help although I doubt he knows the word—the word, help, I mean."

"Good," I replied, "He has an appointment in one week. You bring him up or come along and I'll let him make the choice about treatment at that time, so he'll feel he still has some control."

There was silence for a while as Mike thought it over. "Okay," he said, "I'll do it. I'll take an hour to prepare myself and hope we don't get at each other. I can handle once every month or two." Maybe I should tell Mike about the advantages of jogging, I thought.

Mike brought Howard to the next appointment. I started Howard on prednisone and azathioprine and told him I needed to see him again in six weeks. "I'll try to get back," he groused self-importantly, "but only if I can find the time. You know I'm a busy guy." His wife smiled; his son rolled his eyes; the new housekeeper chuckled. She had come along to sit with Howard on the back seat and distract him and she seemed better able to cope than the last one. Her sense of humor helped.

What a project. It took three people working together to get this bad-tempered old man in for treatment and to take his medicines on a regular schedule. I wondered if he might begin to mellow gradually with all the attention.

Not so. When I saw Howard with his wife and son six weeks later, he was furious. His rage was directed at me and not his son. He looked like he might burst. His usually pink face had turned brick red.

"Your lab kept me waiting one hour before doing my test. Why do I need it anyway?" Fury seemed to be his normal state.

I quietly explained the importance of monitoring for side effects and added, "I see you walked in without a cane."

"Oh, yeah, I guess that's right. I haven't used it for the last week," he said. "I'm walking pretty good and I even dress myself. You got lucky with your medicine."

"I sure did," I said, trying not to grin. "We'll start cutting back on your prednisone and I'll see you in two months to check on how you're doing. I want to make sure you're not having any side effects. Are you okay with that?"

"Well, I'm not okay with that. I don't like this coming back again and again. It's a long drive and I have better things to do than travel and then sit and wait for your damn blood tests," he answered.

I decided to show some authority, to see how he would respond, so while I wrote out his prescriptions I said, softly, "There's enough here to last you two months. I suppose you'll have to come back to get some more. I'm not giving you any refills."

He scowled at me. "Well, if it's still working and I'm still walking, I guess I will see you in two months. Oh, and by the way," he added grudgingly, carefully buttoning his jacket as he stood to leave, "thanks."

The Tattoo

HE SPOKE SLOWLY, pronouncing each syllable with care in his sonorous voice, "I come up from Matewan." He was tall and powerfully built—and he looked like a real mountain man with long, straight brown hair that hung down to his shoulders. He made my exam room seem too small. But there was something about his deeply set blue eyes and low-pitched voice that gave me a sense of profound sadness. "Getting up here from Mingo County is a long haul. We left at 3 o'clock in the morning. It was black as coal. The trip took forever."

I guessed it did. Mingo County is as far as you can get from Morgantown and still be in West Virginia. It is in the southwest corner of the state on the Tug Fork River just across from Kentucky. You travel a lot of winding, two-lane roads before you finally get to the big interstate that takes you north.

"I'm Anderson," he said, holding out his hand. "People call me Anse."

Anse. Now there was a unique nickname. I'd heard it used only once before and it was a name well entrenched in West Virginia history.

"You're not related to 'Devil Anse' Hatfield?" I asked. "He was from Mingo."

"They say I am, they do. They say I got Hatfield blood runnin' in me."

Mingo is the newest county in West Virginia and its history is rich with stories of the Hatfield and McCoy feud in the late 1800s—mostly begun, so the story goes, over the disputed ownership of a razorback hog. The raging family feud caught the country's attention at the time and is still part of West Virginia lore.

"That was a bad time for the Hatfields," Anse said. "Both sides lost a lot of good men." He turned to his wife, who was sitting next to him. "Peggy's a McCoy and her family didn't come out of it no better."

Anse and Peggy sat close to each other on the only two chairs in the exam room, against the wall to one side of the small writing table. She was a small woman with a sweet, gentle way about her. She sat quietly, lovingly caressing Anse's left hand. Anse hadn't moved it the whole time I'd been in the exam room and I could see it was atrophied.

"I'm a coal miner," Anse said. "At least, I used to be. I ain't worked since I got shot two years ago."

A Hatfield, married to a McCoy, working as a coal miner, and getting shot—his story seemed to mirror the whole violent history of this rural county.

The freewheeling feud lasted over thirty years of skirmishes and outright shooting wars between the two clans, ending at the close of the 1800s. Big coal came in at that time. Mining coal—a tough life in a poor, rural county—and coal mining is still the major industry of Mingo County and an integral part of the history of Matewan. The town was founded in 1895 with the opening of the coalfields. Not much industry there before; families like the Hatfields and the McCoys had mostly lived off the land.

In the early 1900s, the United Mine Workers attempted to organize the area's miners. There was a bloody confrontation involving the coal miners and their families against the mine company detectives. Those miners who joined the union's efforts were fired and evicted from their company-owned homes. Shooting was the way to solve problems in those days, and sometimes today, as well.

So here was Anse, a Hatfield descendent and a coal miner, or, at least, had been a coal miner until his left arm injury. "My doctor thought it was time I saw a neurologist about my arm," Anse said. "I can't move it real good. My hand is worthless, but I can move my left shoulder a little."

I said, "Slip off your shirt and tell me how it happened."

He smiled ruefully. "Well, I got shot in the shoulder two years ago. They dug the bullet out right away but it didn't seem to do much good. It ain't got no better since then. And the pain ain't let up one bit either. If anything, it's gotten a whole lot worse. I still gotta' take a lot of pain killers. The boss has been real good to me. He lets me work in the office but the pay ain't hardly as good. Peggy's got to work takin' care of old folks at the nursing home so's we can make ends meet. "

He looked at his wife. She smiled as she got up to help him unbutton his red and black checked flannel work shirt and slip it off. Standing there in front of him she looked even smaller than when they'd been sitting together. The tall and muscular Anse towered over his wife. His muscles were all well sculptured—he looked like an Adonis—except for his left arm that was a flabby caricature of his right

I noticed several bold homemade tattoos on his arms. The muscles of his left arm were all atrophic and his left hand was deformed. He couldn't move the hand or his fingers. He could lift his arm only at the shoulder. Sensation in his arm was almost gone. On the inside of his shoulder I could see the small white scar that was the site of the bullet entry.

When I finished, he asked, "What do you think, Doc?"

"We'll talk about it later, after I get the results of a nerve conduction and EMG test," I said, "it's an electrical test of the nerves and muscles in your arm."

"I'm ready," Anse responded. "Let's do it."

The study showed what I anticipated. In the left arm, the motor and sensory nerve action potentials were either tiny or non-existent. Fibrillations were abundantly present in all muscles of the arm and voluntary motor unit potentials were few and far between. It meant that many of the nerve fibers in the arm had been destroyed.

I decided he needed to know what had happened so he could realize why the damage was so bad and not improving. "I think the bullet went through the brachial plexus," I explained. "The brachial plexus is a network of nerve fibers. It's like a complex electric switching station. These nerve fibers, when they leave the spinal cord in the neck get together and form the plexus. Coming out of the plexus are all the nerves that supply the arm. An injury to the brachial plexus is not a good thing because there's no other way for messages to get from the brain to the arm. It interferes with moving the arm; it messes up the feeling and can cause a lot of pain and eventually, the muscles atrophy. The test we just ran shows there has been massive damage to the nerve. Most of the muscles in the arm have lost their nerve supply."

He nodded his head in understanding. "The doc at home said the same thing," he said, "but not as straight. Can you fix it or make it better?"

"No, I don't think so," I answered. "Trying to hook up all the separated nerves in the plexus with surgery never works."

"I was afraid that would be the answer," he responded. "My arm is so useless, I wish I could just cut it off but doc said we couldn't do that." I nodded my head. "I appreciate your seein' me." He turned to his wife, "Honey, can you help me on with my shirt?"

As I watched her dutifully get up to help him, I wondered about his story. He didn't seem like a battling Hatfield and she was obviously a caring wife—no McCoy woman, she. Or, at least, I didn't think so.

"Anse," I said, "I forgot to ask you, how did you get shot?"

There was a long moment of silence before he answered. His wife stopped between buttons. Her hands seemed frozen as she looked intently at his shirt pocket. "My wife shot me with my gun," he answered in his deliberate, gentle voice.

Nobody moved—not Anse, not Peggy, not me—"But why?" I finally asked, barely above a whisper.

Anse and Peggy remained immobile for what seemed forever as he looked at her. Then he turned to me and said, "You gotta' understand, Doc. Peggy's a good woman, she's the best. I don't know what I'd do without her. But I'd been fooling around with a neighbor lady. She was awful sexy lookin' and I'd sneak off to go drinkin' with her. I didn't have no religion then. Peggy caught me in bed with her and she got pretty mad. I didn't even know she knew how to use a gun but she did. I figure I deserved it. My mom and the preacher said the same thing. I been a good boy since. You can bet I'll never do nothin' like that again."

After a few more moments, Peggy gently helped Anse put his paralyzed arm into the sleeve of his shirt. As she did, the large, homemade tattoo on his left forearm stood out. It said, in bold letters, "Born to lose."

Never Saw it Coming

FRED NEVER WAS very strong, so it was not clear when his weakness began. He was in his early forties when I first saw him.

As he sat on the exam table in his underwear that first day, loosely covered by a white sheet, he looked like a man who had avoided strenuous activities all his life. His face, arms and legs were thin and spindly, belying the fact that he had worked in the construction trade for years. The give-away was his coloring—the exposed parts of his body were nut brown from years of labor in the summer sun, the pale and pasty appearance of his chest and upper arms showed the clear outline of his perennial T-shirt. His lackluster physique seemed to mirror his personality and the nature of his complaint.

His chest musculature was sparse although his breasts were surprisingly large. His abdomen pouched out over his shorts. He had the resigned, stoop-shouldered look of someone who knows good things never happen.

"I've been a carpenter ever since I got out of high school, but over the last few years I've been having trouble hanging on to nails and my tools—they seem to slip out of my fingers. My wife says my speech is a little slurred, too. Everything just seems to be getting a little worse but real, real slow. I come to find out from you what's wrong."

He said it all matter-of-factly with no seeming concern or emotion. His eyes were half closed and focused on the door behind me.

I looked at his wife, who was sitting on a chair in silence. She was a plain-looking woman in a simple housedress. Everything about her was colorless. She was not wearing any makeup, her hair was pale brown, streaked with gray, and her eyes were faded gray in color and looked to be without lashes. She just sat; rigid and unsmiling, hands folded in her lap, watching me. She never said a word, either in response to my initial greeting, or on her own when I included her in the conversation, even though she had plenty of opportunity. I turned back to the patient. "Anything else bothering you?" I asked Fred.

"No," he answered, "except a little trouble swallowing."

"Anyone in your family with anything like this?" I asked.

"No," he answered again, "I have two boys in their teens and they're okay." As we talked, I watched the small brief twitches in his arms and legs and in his chin. There was no pattern to these fasciculations—just random quick bursts of activity, like lightning bugs in the evening sky.

The conversation lagged as I focused my attention on the fasciculations. Fred looked down at his arm. "It's funny about those things," he said. "Every time I look, they're there but I can't feel them jump."

I went on to examine him in more detail. Sensation was normal and reflexes were hard to get. He moved about without difficulty but his rounded, sagging abdomen showed he could eat his dinner just fine but the food wasn't building any muscles. Later that morning, I ran an electromyogram. The result suggested that his motor neurons were degenerating. It was not a surprise.

There it was. Gradually developing weakness, muscle wasting, and fasciculations—all this was easily observable and then corroborated by the electrical tests of the muscles.

I explained the findings to him and to his wife, "The problem is similar to Lou Gehrig's disease but much less severe. Your breasts are enlarged, and that raises the possibility of Kennedy's disease." I gave them some basic information about the disorder and suggested that we do a genetic test to confirm the diagnosis. Fred wearily nodded agreement.

Kennedy's disease is a genetic disorder, named after William Kennedy, a Minnesota neurologist, which causes the motor neurons in the brain stem and spinal cord to degenerate. These cells supply the nerve fibers that innervate the muscle fibers. As these neurons deteriorate, patients lose muscle fibers resulting in weakness and wasting, especially the tongue and those muscles that control swallowing, and those in the arms. The fasciculations are a hallmark of the dying motor neurons and are easy to spot. Kennedy's disease occurs only in men who inherit the abnormal gene from their unaffected carrier mothers. The enlarged breasts are caused by the abnormal gene interfering with the function of androgens, the male sex hormone.

When I saw Fred several weeks later the results were back and, as I had suspected, were consistent with the diagnosis of Kennedy's disease. Fred seemed little interested in this news, but his wife spoke to me, it seemed for the first time. Her voice was flat. "Does that mean there is some treatment to help Fred?"

I knew I had been avoiding what was the main issue for the patient. Neither Fred nor his wife cared much what the disease was; they wanted to know what it meant for them, and quite rightly so. "No, there is no effective treatment," I answered. "I wish there were. Having the diagnosis only means we have a better understanding of what is happening. Unfortunately, there is nothing we can do to stop or even to slow down motor neuron degeneration."

"I suppose he could have passed this on to our boys..." Fred's wife half said, half asked, her face expressionless while she looked down at her lap.

"No, there is no chance that Fred could have passed it on to your sons. If you had a daughter, she could be a carrier and then she could pass it on to a son. But father to son, it never happens." I decided to avoid any detailed discussion of sex-linked inheritance. "The boys are safe. This illness ends with Fred."

I thought she might smile with relief but she just nodded her head, still looking down, not at me or at Fred. I turned to him and put my hand on his shoulder.

"I'd like to see you every three to six months, Fred, so I can help you deal with any problems that might arise, like having more trouble with your arms and legs or more problems with swallowing. We may need the physical therapist to show you how to make better use of your arms."

"Okay," he said, after a long pause. "Then, like you said, I guess I'll see you in a few months." He got up slowly. We shook hands as he left. His grasp was soft, with little pressure. When I let go his hand, his arm dropped to his side. His wife made no move to shake my hand, just nodded at me without a word or a smile.

I saw Fred every six months for many years after that. He always said he was doing fine when I asked how he was, to which his wife always silently shook her head. We never talked about anything except his weakness and he would always answer questions in a passive and seemingly disinterested way. He never made eye contact with me. I graded the strength of his muscles at each visit. He got weaker, almost imperceptibly slowly. Working became more difficult and he finally applied for disability.

Fred's wife was there each time. I never saw the two sons. She was sober as ever and always quiet, except to say at every visit, "I think he's weaker than the last time you saw him."

I knew she had to be worried about the future although she never voiced it. Assuming this to be true, my answer was always, "His strength seems about the same, but compared to two years ago he does seem a little weaker." I silently hoped that her unvoiced concern about his ultimate incapacitation was unfounded.

As the years went by, I noticed that Fred's speech was becoming more slurred as a result of the increasing weakness of his tongue and lips. Swallowing too was becoming more difficult. He had no trouble breathing, but he no longer had a strong cough. I worried that he might have problems with aspiration down the road.

My concern turned out to be groundless. To my relief, Fred never lost his ability to walk or to perform his daily activities. He just seemed to keep winding down—slowly. Although his speech became difficult to understand, he always managed to swallow without choking on food or liquids.

TWENTY YEARS AFTER I had first seen Fred, I ran into his wife in the hospital corridor. I was making rounds and she appeared, walking swiftly and purposefully—with her head up. Her energy was amazing and for a second I wasn't sure she was the same person I knew. I was surprised she was alone—I'd never seen her without Fred. I suddenly realized I'd never learned her name. She stopped when she saw me. "Hello, is Fred okay?" I asked.

"No," she answered, "he's been here the last four days. He died all of a sudden this morning. I'm on my way to make the final arrangements."

I was dumbfounded by the news and amazed that she was so calm and showed so little grief. "Nobody called me to see him," I said, incredulously. "I had no idea he was in trouble."

"No, no, the problem wasn't his muscle disease," she said. "I thought, at first, it was. He was so short of breath—I was afraid he'd stop breathing altogether—and he had some chest pain so I brought him in as an emergency in the middle of the night. They said he had a heart attack and that it was huge. They did everything but he never had a chance." And, for the first time in twenty years, she looked directly at me and smiled—an unbelievably warm and friendly smile.

"You know," she continued, "all these years I lived in constant fear for Fred, worrying that he would end up an invalid, unable to care for himself, lying there unable to eat, unable to move, and having trouble breathing. I was sure his dying would be slow and awful. I didn't know how I'd manage. I spent the past twenty years in dread. And then this happened. It came out of nowhere. We never saw it coming."

Flat Tire

THE LONG EVENING shadows were beginning to stretch across the trail. The late afternoon sun seemed to explode into an infinite number of sparkles off the Monongahela River. I was near the end of my evening bike ride—closing down after a busy day in the clinic. The oppressive heat of summer had lifted and cool breezes promised that fall was coming. The dense green foliage of the forest floor framing the trail was punctuated by a mélange of colors—wild yellow sunflowers and goldenrod, the dusty rose of the towering Joe-Pye weed, white goat's beard and Queen Anne's lace, and the intense purple of the occasional ironweed and bull thistles.

As I rode, I replayed the day's clinic, picturing and sorting out the patients and their families—some old friends, some new referrals—all hoping for help and understanding and, for the new ones, finding the cause of their problem. One young woman's image dominated my thoughts. What began as a straightforward case of cerebral palsy had turned into a moving and heartrending story.

The soft crunch of my bike tires rolling over the fine pea gravel was interrupted by a sudden hissing sound. I looked down and saw the back bike tire begin to flatten. My right hand automatically squeezed the brake handle. The day had been full of challenges and here was one last one—half an hour patching a flat tire. My momentary annoyance was replaced by thoughts of Stephanie's quandary.

She'd been the first patient of the morning. I watched her walk down the hall from the waiting area. An older woman and my office assistant walked slowly along side her. She watched the floor as she maneuvered stiffly toward the exam room. The awkward swing of her legs and the unusual angle of her left arm magnified the effort she was making.

I looked at the referral sheet and scanned through her medical record. She was 23, had cerebral palsy, and her memory was said to be deteriorating. The medical student working with me kept watching her as she disappeared into the room.

"I know her from someplace," he said. "She looks so familiar. I wish I could remember where I've seen her." I let it pass.

After a time, I tapped on the exam room door. The medical student and I went in to join the patient and the woman with her, who was her mother. Stephanie struggled up from the chair to shake hands with me. Her mother smiled briefly, nodding her head, but kept her gaze fixed on her daughter. The young woman sat down and immediately slumped in her chair, her sandy curly hair pulled back and tied in a short ponytail with a doubled blue rubber band. Some strands were scattered at random in different directions as if she had gotten ready to go out without looking in the mirror. Stephanie was a bit overweight, and this, together with her sad expression, detracted from her otherwise pretty face.

"I'm here," she began with a sorrowful look, "because I'm having so much trouble remembering. The doctors at home say it might be a dementia but the medicines they put me on didn't help. In fact, the drugs made it worse and made me gain 70 pounds. They've done MRI scans of everything and tested my memory and they say my cerebral palsy's getting worse. Not only that, I've been diagnosed with fibromyalgia and..."

Once started, she went on and on with a welter of second-hand opinions from other physicians and test results, but nothing she said was very helpful. She was taking me in the wrong direction, like a traffic officer signaling a left turn when you want to go right. I put my hand up for her to pause. "I think I'd like to start from the beginning. Can you tell me the details of how your symptoms developed? Can you and your mom talk about the first few years of your life?"

She turned slowly to look at her mother and then back toward me. She never smiled. Her melancholy seemed to overwhelm the room. "Well, to start with I was born two months early and was the first of twins," Stephanie said.

"I kept telling the doctor," her mother interjected, "but he wouldn't believe there were twins 'til they were born." I could sense a touch of sadness and resignation in her voice, any anger having dissipated long ago.

"Both babies were sent here," her Mom continued. "Stephanie only weighed three pounds and she was in the ICU six weeks before I could take her home. Her brother died at three weeks. Stephanie is our only child. My husband and I have devoted ourselves to doing everything we can for her."

"Tell me about Stephanie's developmental milestones," I asked. "When did she begin talking and walking?"

"There was never a problem with her talking," she said, "but she didn't take her first steps 'til she was two. It's always been a struggle for her. Over the years, she had a lot of operations on her legs. They lengthened tendons, moved some muscles and even fused her left ankle."

"I really manage pretty good," Stephanie said. It was the first time she looked or sounded positive about anything.

"How did you do with your studies?" I asked, not sure whether Stephanie or her mother would answer.

"Stephanie won't tell you but she's always been a good student," her mother was taking the lead. "She was a scholarship student here at the university. She always made the honor roll and graduated a year ago."

A college graduate? For a moment, I stopped writing notes in her medical record and looked up. "The honor roll—you weren't having any memory problems then," I said, looking at Stephanie. There had been no clues that a scholar's mind lay hidden beneath her depressed appearance.

"No, not then," she said. "My trouble remembering didn't start 'til after I began medical school."

The surprises kept on coming. I decided to stop writing and put down my pen. I waited, looking from one to the other and finally back to Stephanie. The room was suddenly silent except for some distant murmurs coming from the nursing station.

"I had to take a leave of absence after seven weeks," Stephanie said softly. "There was so much to learn and so much to memorize. I really felt overwhelmed. It was so much harder than college. I had to study all the time and then I had trouble sleeping. After a while, nothing made sense. I couldn't concentrate, I couldn't remember, it all got mixed up. I really tried, Mom even moved into my apartment for the last few weeks to help with all the household things—we both wanted to make a success out of med school. The fact I missed the first three days of classes didn't help. We were in a car accident coming up from home. Nothing serious but I did bang my head and hurt my shoulder. It was pretty scary. The doctors in the ED said I was okay." She began to cry quietly. The medical student working with me handed her a tissue.

"So you dropped out of school?" Stephanie nodded. "What have you been doing the past year?" I asked.

Stephanie wiped her eyes. "I've been staying at home with my mom and dad."

"She spends a lot of time with her dog," her mother said.

"Have you tried working or taking classes?" I asked.

"The memory problem makes doing anything impossible, I'm awake half the night, and I'm tired all the time," Stephanie said. "I thought about a part-time job but I'd lose my health insurance—I'm covered by my mom and dad's plan.

Spending time with her dog at home, no effort to even volunteer, no mention of reading—Stephanie was just vegetating. Why had she decided to quit? Her physical infirmities had never stopped her before. Had medical school been too much of a challenge for her, and had the stress of the accident played a role?

Her mother handed me a formal written evaluation made the previous fall by our neuropsychologists. The report indicated that Stephanie had done all the tasks of the tests well, although at times she lost her concentration, and this very likely reflected her depression. They felt her intelligence was well above average but less than expected in a medical student. There were no changes to suggest the she had a dementia.

When it was time for the physical, Stephanie moved determinedly to the exam table. Her foot motions were awkward, especially those on the left. Her left hand, when held outstretched, assumed a contorted posture. I gave her some mental tasks and she performed them slowly but flawlessly. She knew the date and where she was. Her knowledge of current events was excellent. She correctly spelled the word, "world," backwards, without hesitation and remembered three words I gave her—apple, bicycle, and Park Street—after ten minutes.

While Stephanie got dressed, the student and I left the room to view the MRI scan of her brain made several months earlier.

The ventricles were larger than expected in a 23-year-old woman and there was scarring deep in the right hemisphere of the brain. The cortex of her brain was untouched by the insult she'd sustained so many years ago.

"Her brain took a real hit when she was born," I said, "but there's a lot more to her problem."

"You know," the student said, "I realized when we were in the room how I know her." For a moment I thought he was changing the subject. "We took several biology courses at the university together, before we came to med school. They were big classes, so I'm not surprised she doesn't remember me. Stephanie was good but no one in the class worked as hard as she did. Any time I was in the library, she was there studying. I think her whole life was school."

I nodded my head; interesting information, I thought. Her academic accomplishments had been her constant source of courage in the face of physical adversity. She'd worked hard to achieve success. She'd likely given it her maximum effort. The intense challenges of medical school could have been one step too far, and maybe the traffic accident had added intolerably to the burden.

Stillness had settled over the room when we returned. Stephanie and her mother watched me expectantly as I pulled up the stool and sat down. The student stood behind me, leaning against the metal cabinet.

"As a neurologist," I began, "I have to say I can't find anything wrong to explain your memory loss, insomnia, and low energy. Your problems with walking and clumsiness as well as the MRI abnormalities date back decades. At the same time, these are all static problems. There's nothing to suggest any worsening of your cerebral palsy and the neuropsychological test showed no signs of dementia." I told her that a serious depression was the most likely explanation for her symptoms.

"That's good news, but what is our next step? Her mother asked.

I leaned forward as we talked about other students who found medical school a struggle and the pain and distress of having their hopes and dreams shattered—that medical school is much more intense and demanding than college and sometimes it doesn't take much to tip the balance.

I paused for a moment and then continued, "You've dealt with your neurologic deficits effectively and your academic achievements are impressive. You really worked hard to succeed." I was thinking about my third-year medical student's observation of Stephanie's classroom diligence. "You're like the fine college basketball player who's having difficulty in the pros. This doesn't take anything away from how well you have done, but you need to stop and take another look at where you're going. You need some counseling to help you decide about your future. Perhaps medical school is still for you. Maybe it's worth another try, now that you know what you're up against—that it isn't just an extension of college. If it doesn't work out, there are other areas in the healing professions to consider. Whatever you decide to do, you're an intelligent person and you need to get on with your life.

THE SUN WAS beginning to set as I finished patching my bike tire and began blowing it up with my small black air pump. A long train, silver colored cars filled with black coal, rolled by on the other side of the river, the twin engines blasting their whistle. I quickly got the repaired bike wheel attached. My tire was perfectly good again and I felt an intense sense of accomplishment. I thought about Stephanie's academic successes in

college and how hard she had to work but what an important
sense of her own worth she had from that success. The rigors
of medical school had punctured that feeling. If she tried again,
could she now do it? Was medical school worth another try?
Was it a goal that made sense for her? She could bring a great
sympathy and understanding of patients with infirmities to her
role as physician if she continued, and that could count for a
lot. As I pedaled off, a full moon was beginning to rise above
the nearby ridge.

The Coal Miner

"The following operations of Consolidation Coal will work the afternoon shift: the Arkwright Mine, the Osage Mine, the Humphrey Mine, the Pursglove Mine, and the Blacksville Number 2 Mine..." The message came crackling over the radio in Morgantown. It was broadcast every day, as routine as the notification of school closings after a snowstorm.

THREE MAJOR DISASTERS defined Gary Gallatin's life—an explosion, a mine accident, and a stroke. I met him for the first time after the third and final disaster. He lay quietly on the hospital gurney with his head elevated, looking straight ahead. He was 59 years old. The room was still except for his stertorous breathing. His thick gray hair was tousled; random clumps extending in all directions. His full, squared-off face showed no concern or emotion, almost to the point of seeming indifferent. He quietly watched his wife and daughter as they provided all the information about the past 18 hours while I examined him. The CT scan showed a large area of hypodensity in the pons—a major part of the brain stem—that told a dire story.

The devastating pontine abnormality had all the characteristics of an acute stroke and accounted for his sudden loss of muscle strength and coordination. However, the changes in the brain stem were much less remarkable than the large areas of missing brain in his frontal lobes. These had all the appearance of an extensive pre-frontal lobotomy—an operation used a half century ago on schizophrenic and combative patients. A large metal plate, visible on the CT scan and replacing the frontal bone, could only mean that there'd been major trauma in the past. His old forehead scars and missing left eye gave further evidence of the prior injury. I spent time with his wife and daughter piecing together the history of his previous disasters.

Gary grew up in a small southwestern Pennsylvania town, He was the oldest of six children; his father was a coal miner and his mother worked in a shirt factory. His wife said friends described him as a nice guy who spent considerable time helping his mother care for his younger siblings.

The first tragedy happened when Gary was 16. Without warning, the coal stove in the living room exploded. Gary was upstairs with his mother and baby sister when the house was engulfed in flames and smoke. He pushed his mother out the window and jumped after her but, before he could stop her, his mother ran back into the house, now flaming like a tinderbox, to try to save the other children. Gary watched helplessly as his five brothers and sisters and his mother perished in the raging fire. Gary's father, Leland, was working in the Shannopin Mine that afternoon. Of his large family, only Gary remained.

Gary became withdrawn after the tragedy but, with time, he put it behind him and, after finishing high school, he married his high school sweetheart, Dorothy. Like his father, he became a coal miner. He was proud to follow in Leland's footsteps.

In the 1960s and 1970s coal mining was a dominant part of the economic and social structure of West Virginia's Monongalia County and surrounding areas. Coal was king. And in the late nineteenth and early twentieth centuries, mining provided opportunities for desperate non-English-speaking immigrants—Italians, Hungarians, Czechs, and Poles—willing to work for meager wages in unsafe conditions. West Virginia's history is replete with mining disasters and tragedies. Although sophisticated mining machines and strict government safety rules and regulations have replaced the pick and shovel days, accidents continue to occur.

Dorothy described Gary at 24 as trim and muscular with brown hair, cut neat and short. "He was good natured and always had a ready smile," Dorothy said. "We were married four years before the accident. He enjoyed being a father. The baby was three when the accident happened. Tammy—her middle name Leann was in memory of one of his sisters who'd died in the fire—was a great joy and Gary spent many long hours helping to care for her. It was a role he had missed since the house had burned so many years ago. He had such great patience with her. He did everything she wanted to make her happy. He was the perfect husband and the perfect father."

Consol's Blacksville #2, a union mine, had just become operational and Gary and Eugene, Dorothy's brother, began working there in late 1970. Eugene remembered his young brother-in-law as a conscientious and hard worker who was easy-going and accommodating, often working overtime. "He liked to have fun. He was always neat and particular, especially about his car. He always kept it clean."

When Gary began work in the mine, he hired on as a roof bolter. He knew securing the roof to prevent cave-ins was the most dangerous job in any mine and also one of the best paying. Gary liked the challenge of operating the machine—setting up safety jacks to support the roof, drilling holes into the several layers of rock strata, and setting four-foot rods into the mine ceiling.

Gary never remembered how it happened when the roof crashed down. His foreman had asked him to work through the lunch hour, to finish bolting up an offset in two roof heights. Suddenly a slab of coal broke free, hitting Gary's helmet and forcing his face into the front of the bolting machine. Eugene found him moments later. Gary was unconscious, blood seeping from his nose and ears, his face and forehead crushed flat. After Gary was rushed to the hospital, Eugene looked over the scene. "There was just a small pile of coal on the floor—about a wheelbarrow load. You never would have guessed that it'd almost killed Gary."

Dorothy told me, "After the surgery his neurosurgeon told me that Gary's left side would be paralyzed and, if he survived, he would probably end up not able to do anything for himself."

Dorothy, young and idealistic, could not accept this grim prognosis and devoted herself to caring for Gary in the hospital. She helped bathe him, massaging his skin, and exercising his arms and legs. It took weeks before he slowly began regaining consciousness. Gary spent the next year in an intensive rehabilitation program and underwent reconstructive cranial and facial surgery.

Dorothy's dark haired, fun-loving and smiling, handsome husband had been transformed. He was moody and withdrawn and there were unpredictable outbursts of frustration. Dorothy couldn't remember his ever being angry or losing his temper before, but now it was a regular event. Complicating everything were grand mal seizures, made worse by his refusal to take his medications.

As the years went by, Gary's moodiness and impatience began to dissipate and his ever-ready smile returned. Still, as Dorothy said, "The accident changed everything." Gary's life as a hard working young coal miner was now behind him. No more long hours in the in the dark coal pits. Listening to the afternoon shift announcements on the radio—a part of every coal miner's life—was long forgotten. Once Gary recovered physically, he never tired of spending his days visiting with his long-time friends and hanging out in his hometown of Mt. Morris, a small working community nestled in the foothills of the Appalachians.

For many years Gary's days had centered on the floral and beauty shop on Main Street that his wife, Dorothy, owned. For several hours every day, he entertained the women who worked there with his jokes and stories. The Senior Center, where he often took lunch, played bingo and checkers, and participated in sing-alongs, was just around the corner. It was only a short walk to O'Reilly's Pub, a green and white cinderblock building right on the edge of the highway, where he liked playing pool and watching NASCAR races and eating cheeseburgers and French fries.

To family and neighbors, Gary always seemed laid-back, easy-going and relaxed. His continuous smile and his droopy eye-lid gave him the mischievous look of someone permanently winking at the world. His soft, overweight body gave no hint of the muscular young coal miner of years ago. He was happy when friends took him along on shopping expeditions or to the local pond for fishing. Tammy recalled him, as she was growing up, more as a playmate than a dad. She didn't remember him as he had been before the mine roof crashed down.

"He would hold the end of the rope so I could jump, be the back seat rider on our two-seat bike, and pitch the softball to me. I can never remember him being angry with me or disciplining me. In fact, when I got in trouble with mom I would run to him to take up for me, and he always did. I could never do anything wrong in his eyes, both as a child and as an adult. He never helped me with my homework or showed me how to drive. What he did teach me, though, was to enjoy what life gives you and not cry about what might have been."

Dorothy, his wife, saw him clearly as a man with no real initiative, no motivation, and no ambition, but she was still devoted to him. Gary took no interest in his personal hygiene and had to be reminded to brush his teeth and shower. He felt no responsibility in doing any of the household chores. He would pay others to mow the grass or wash the car rather then do it himself.

In many ways the transformation in Gary was like that in the well publicized case of Phineas Gage, the capable and efficient railway foreman who, in 1848, had a tamping iron explode through the frontal portion of his brain. The personality changes in both men were profound but with a difference. While Gary became docile and indifferent, Gage became impatient, irreverent, and grossly profane. The dissimilarity in the two patients related to differences in frontal lobe structures destroyed

"When I learn how to walk again, first thing I'll do is go fishin' with my dad" he would tell the therapist every day while going through his rehabilitation, "Leland's gonna' take me to Canada."

On one of Leland's occasional visits, all Gary wanted to talk about was the trip. "Hey, dad," Gary said. "I'm walking real good. I should be ready to go fishing in a few weeks. We're still goin' to Canada, right?" His pallid face was red with excitement.

On this visit, Leland's last, he stood, looking down at his work shoes. Leland was a small man with dark curly hair and a thin, neatly trimmed moustache. Dorothy, sitting quietly in the corner, leaned forward, watching him intently.

"Well, yea," Leland said, still looking down. "I am goin'
to Canada this summer but I'm gonna' be there to fish, not to
baby sit."

Gary smiled, nodding his head. Leland's words were lost on
him. He was only glad Leland had come to see him.

Not Dorothy, who was instantly furious. She suddenly
came out of her chair, her face beet red. "You get out of here,
right now," she yelled at him, pushing Leland toward the open
doorway behind him, "and don't you ever come back. If Gary
wants to fish in Canada, I'll take him."

Years later, when Tammy was a teenager, she drove Gary to
the cemetery to put flowers on the family graves. Dorothy had
picked them out carefully—a large colorful wreath for Gary's
mom and small bouquets for each of the children—and Tammy
helped him carry them.

Going to the cemetery memorialized the first great tragedy
in Gary's life—a disaster that he never would talk about
but one Dorothy knew he remembered on some level. "Are you
going to be all right?" Dorothy asked every year but Gary
would just give a long sigh with other real sign of any emotion.

This Memorial Day, two decades after the fire, a man came
toward Gary and Tammy on the path. Gary recognized him.

"How you doin'?"

"OK," the man answered.

"Everything all right?"

The man nodded and walked on.

"Who was that?" Tammy asked. "I've never seen him
before."

"Oh," Gary answered blandly, "that was my dad." Gary
kept on walking.

It was the last time Gary saw Leland and the first time
Tammy had seen her grandfather. "I think he missed having a

relationship with his dad," Tammy said, describing the incident to me, "I think he was an embarrassment to Leland."

The day after I first met Gary in the hospital, he quietly slipped into a coma. The stroke involving his pons had enlarged despite our attempts to contain it. It now had extended to the brain stem area that controls consciousness. Dorothy sat quietly at his bedside, holding his immobile hand in a gentle embrace. Tammy stood in the corner, off to one side, watching intently.

"He's had such a hard life," Dorothy said, her voice barely audible. "It doesn't seem fair."

"It's been hard and unfair for both of you," I said. "You lived the last 30 years with a man you didn't marry—a man completely changed by a terrible accident. A lot of people wouldn't have done it. Many people wouldn't have stayed."

She smiled as tears slowly streamed down her cheeks. She gently squeezed Gary's hand. A lifetime of memories seemed to be passing before her eyes. She'd married the man of her dreams only to have it all come crashing down on her.

At first, she was his nurse and then she became the sole support of their little family. She worked as a medical transcriptionist and managed her own flower and beauty shop and she was a homeroom mom, Brownie leader, and a chaperone on school field trips. All the while she took care of Gary.

"I was committed to him. It was the right thing to do," Dorothy said through her tears.

Tammy's response was different. "People ask me if I regret not knowing my dad before the mining accident. I've never known how to answer that. The truth is that you can't miss someone you never knew. He was a simple man but, at the same time, an extraordinary one who knew how to make the most out of what life dishes out. That's what I always say, he taught me, to enjoy what life can give you and not cry about what might have been."

Following each mining accident in West Virginia, there is always serious governmental and public scrutiny of the safety regulations that affect coal miners. Gary's accident resulted in several regulations including requiring a steel canopy to cover the bolting machine and two men working on the machine at any one time.

Doing It Right On Ambler Ridge
KEITH WOLFE 1917 – 2003

IF YOU HAD ASKED Keith Wolfe to name the most important things about his life he'd probably have told you, first, that
he was born in 1917 in Walton, West Virginia, out on the Poca
River Road, in Roane County. That was important because the
period around 1917 was the heyday of the oil boom in Roane
County and Keith's father, Clarence, worked in the Rock Creek
Oil Field. The Walton of Keith's boyhood was a busy town, "I
think there were more people living there then than do now,"
Keith remembered.

"The first oil well was drilled in 1904," he said, "and that
was the beginning of the boom that lasted into the Depression.
I remember the town had at least two hotels in those days and
Main Street was just dirt."

"Oil was big then but those were dangerous times." Keith
recalled the Hamiltonia Gasoline Plant on McKown's Creek.
"It was owned by the Hamilton Oil Company. It's good my
father never worked there. The plant would blow up once a
year. They didn't care about safety in those days. And at least
half the people working there didn't know what they was
doing. They didn't know much, didn't have any education, and
came straight off the farm."

Keith went to grade school at the Mt Lebanon School on
Ambler Ridge. It was a two-room schoolhouse with no running

water, "We had to bring our own," Keith said, "and no inside toilets."

Second most important in Keith's life were three notable years of service to his country during World War II. Keith lived in Walton or nearby except for 1942 to 1945 when he was in the Air Force. He was stationed in Newbury, England where he worked as an air traffic controller—"a tower man"—and met Betty, his wife-to-be, an English girl. When the war ended and Keith came home, he lived in Charleston and went to Morris Harvey College part-time for two years on the GI Bill while he worked at FMC Corporation.

Meeting Betty in England was a milestone and the third most important event for Keith—third in time sequence, but perhaps most important to his happiness in life. He and Betty were in love and in 1947, after writing back and forth; she came over to marry him and to live in West Virginia—first in Charleston and then, three years later, in Walton.

Betty was a city girl. She was appalled by her first impressions of the Charleston of a half-century ago. "It was nothing like London. I kept asking, 'Where are the underground stations?' I couldn't understand how people got around. If I could have gotten on the boat right then, I'd have went home." But moving to the farm in Walton changed everything for Betty. Five decades later she said, emphatically, "My roots are here in America."

Another important event in Keith's life occurred in 1950, when he bought his 157 1/4-acre farm (according to his property deed) three miles out of town on Ambler Ridge. Keith Wolfe's house doesn't have a water meter—the same well that has been running for a century still serves. It was drilled in 1907. The house he owns was built before the Civil War.

Keith and Betty lived there for 52 years and brought up their two children. Keith also raised purebred Herefords—as many as 64 head at one time—for 40 years, and grew all his own fodder for them while working at FMC Corporation. Until late in life, when I knew him, Keith still had three cows, three dogs, assorted chickens, rented out his pasture to another farmer, and got an unlimited supply of free natural gas because of 13 oil wells—four of them still work—that dot his farm.

You might ask how Keith managed to work at FMC full-time in Charleston and run his farm in Walton and why he did both. "Well, it wasn't easy," he told me. "I mainly had cattle plus a few hogs and a milk cow. I had to leave for work at six in the morning and haul a bunch of riders with me. In the summer I'd come home from work and cut hay 'til 10 o'clock at night if the moon was shining bright. But I never could have done it without Betty. She was number one. She took care of the kids and the farm by herself when I wasn't there. In the winter, I'd load up the two hay chutes in the barn on the weekends and Betty'd go out every day to spread out the hay in the mangers for the cattle. She did the milking too.

"Now why did I do both—work in Charleston and run the farm? Tell you what, Doc, I was really ambitious. I wanted to outrun and outstrip all my relations——bootleggers, teachers, all of them."

I knew Keith as only his doctor could know him. Over years of visits and conversations we became friends. We first met in the summer of 1996 when he came up from the farm to see me in my clinic. Keith was having problems with muscle weakness.

The first thing I saw in him was his sense of humor. He was holding his jaw up with his thumb as I walked into the examination room and he said immediately, "I know this looks crazy to you, Doc, but I can't keep my mouth shut." He smirked at me and let his jaw drop to show me, while his wife smiled politely. Then he added, "It's been coming and going for two years. The first time I got it, I was driving me and the wife home from my daughter's and I had to hold up my jaw for twenty miles."

It turned out that he also had weakness of his tongue and facial muscles that interfered with his speech and worsened as the day progressed. His arms and legs were not affected. "Yesterday I pitched thirty bales of hay on my farm. Not bad for a seventy-nine-year-old fellow," he told me, grinning with pride.

I saw him as a healthy man with nothing else wrong with him, except for his weakness. His face was tanned brown and wrinkled with deep creases from years of working in the sun. His arms and legs were muscular and he didn't have an extra ounce of fat on him. He was full of energy and good spirits but the muscles of his face and jaw were weak and so was his tongue. Both eyelids drooped and his right eyelid almost completely covered his eye. As I listened to Keith's story and studied his features, I saw a textbook illustration of a rare muscle disease called myasthenia gravis.

I told him that it was an autoimmune disorder—an illness caused by his immune system making antibodies directed at the point where the motor nerves attach to the muscle fibers—the neuromuscular junction. The body produces antibodies to get rid foreign proteins like viruses and bacteria, but occasionally it makes a mistake and creates antibodies against itself. "That's what happens in myasthenia gravis," I said. "In the military they call it friendly fire."

"Well, it doesn't sound so friendly to me but I was sure you'd figure it out," he said. "Now tell me what we're gonna' do about it."

After I got to know him better, I realized this was a typical Keith response. He always had confidence that something good could be done and saw every challenge as winnable.

Keith's optimism was well placed. The medicines commonly used to treat myasthenia gravis—prednisone and azathioprine—suppressed his immune system's attack. Fortunately for Keith the drugs had no side effects and all his muscle weakness gradually disappeared over eight months.

For the next six years Keith came to see me every few months for check-ups. He always came with his daughter or his wife. He may have looked old, but he never seemed old. His enthusiasm for life made me look forward to his visits and seemed to infect everyone else, as well. He liked talking about his family. Every visit brought a new memory or story. One time he told me about his mother, who was a Hawkins and was from Harmony, eight miles west of Walton. "All her original family is buried up there on the F.B.I. property, just off Jerry Dove Drive. The original bunch came out of Ireland." Another time I asked him about his father's family. "I don't know a whole lot about my father's people. A cousin in Ohio told me that one of the first Wolfes came to America from debtor's prison in England."

In 2001 Keith's wife, Betty, stopped coming with him because she was battling cancer. After that, his daughter came instead but one day he was alone. For the first time there was no family member with him. He looked fine, except his smile was somewhat faded. "How's your wife?" I asked.

"Oh, Doc," he answered, "I've had an awful time the last three weeks. She just died of her cancer. I miss her terrible. I thought I'd handle it better, but we were married fifty-four years. She was a good woman."

"It's hard to lose someone you really love," I said, "I remember how close you two were."

He perked up at that, smiled and fished in his pocket. "Doc, let me show you a picture of the tombstone I designed for us." He held up a drawing of it, looking proud.

On the left side of the stone was inscribed, "Keith - 8th and 9th Air Force - WWII." On the right it said, "Betty - English War Bride - WWII."

"You see, this stone gives our life story," he said. "Two hundred years from now people won't have any trouble figuring out what was important."

Betty was buried on a sunny knoll in the private cemetery on their farm. A few other family members are buried there but mostly Keith opened it to neighbors who were too poor to be laid to rest anywhere else. "I got thirteen people buried up there – a 16-year-old boy who rode his motorcycle into the side of a house, his dad who died of a heart attack, a young pretty woman who choked in an asthma attack. I even have two babies buried up there; one was murdered by her mother. They were all broke, all dole jobs."

I asked Keith what was so special about Walton. "I've always loved this part of the county," he told me. "I know everybody and everybody knows me. I may be the best-known man in Walton. And I gotta' tell you, most of the old people are dead now but they were some of the finest people you'd ever want to meet."

Ben Robertson, Keith's long-time friend and CEO of the Poca Valley Bank told a story that typifies this generous man, "Some years ago, after Keith had retired from FMC he told me, 'By God, I was up to my elbows in asbestos but the company did everything they promised they would—gave me a gold watch and a good retirement package, I got no complaints. I think it's awful they way people are trying sue them now.'"

When I visited him at his farm his neighbor had come over to check on him. Keith didn't seem to need any checking on but he sure enjoyed the company. Another day, when I called, I was glad when his grandson told me Keith couldn't talk to me on the phone because he was out on his four-wheeler, working on his farm.

Keith always knew what was important. He did, all his life.

KEITH WOLFE DIED on November 13, 2003, at his home. He was 87 years old and active on his farm until shortly before his death. He spent many long hours helping me do research on the history of Walton. He was laid to rest as he had wished next to his wife, Betty, in his private cemetery on the farm.

Sally and Rosi

IT'S HARD TO KNOW when my mother's dementia began. We first noticed it after my father entered a nursing home, late in both their lives. Had she been managing to keep herself together by sheer force of will when Dad became ill, feeling she had to look out for him? When Mom's responsibility in caring for her husband ended, did her lifelong need to control go with it, never to return?

While my mother's dementia tiptoed in almost unnoticed, my father's was much easier to date. He and my mother had retired and moved from their farm in New Jersey to live near me in Morgantown.

My father seemed to enjoy retirement—taking long walks on the nearby golf course, entertaining his grandchildren, watching the barge traffic move slowly on the Monongahela River, In fact, it wasn't until he was in his late seventies and had an operation on his prostate gland, that his life changed.

The surgery went well but the anesthesia had a disastrous effect. When he woke from the operation he was overwhelmed by visual hallucinations. He saw snakes, bugs, and wild animals. He was terrified—they seemed so real—and the experience lasted for hours. Nothing could console him or persuade him out of it.

His fearful imaginings were also frightening to me, but for another reason. They made me realize my father might have the beginnings of Alzheimer's disease. He had been so healthy, his prostate was a minor problem, and I had fantasized that he could go on as he was forever. The hallucinations brought home for me the realization that the final chapter of his life was beginning. The chemical stress of the anesthesia on his brain had awakened the lethal disease that had been smoldering unnoticed.

When he got out of the hospital—and now that I was looking more carefully—I saw that he was slowing down physically and was also not as quick mentally. He remained his quiet self for some time, perhaps even quieter and less self-confident, letting Mom do all the talking and planning.

When we were growing up, my younger brother, Frank, and I had seen Dad as a powerful, muscular man, his body shaped like a fire hydrant, his head rounded with a dense fringe of white hair. Mom said that in Germany, working as a salesman and, later, as an executive, he'd been soft and flabby, but after their flight to safety in America, farm work had created a physical toughness that remained with him the rest of his life.

My mother said admiringly, "He's a far cry from the overweight man he was in Germany. He was always sick with something over there, but not anymore. Moving to America may have saved his life in more ways than just escaping the Nazis."

Dad's large hands with their stubby fingers were heavily calloused from lifting heavy feed sacks and doing outdoor work in all seasons. His proper name was Salomon but everyone called him Sally. He was a gentle, pleasant, and caring man with friendly, deep-set blue eyes—the color of violets in spring—framed by broadly tufted white brows, and a ready smile. He was a man with a compelling sense of responsibility and this was reflected in his commitment and devotion to us.

Farm work is exhausting. It was an unbelievable change for my parents after their comfortable life in Dresden. And, for Dad, it meant long hours alone doing the work of the farm, but he seemed to relish those solitary, quiet hours even though in public and in general he was charming and outgoing, with an easy laugh and a good word for everyone.

Underneath it all, however, there was a certain angst, a sadness that had to do with his time of military service fighting in the German infantry in World War I and being forced to emigrate from his native country in 1937, at the peak of his business career. He talked as little as possible about these momentous experiences, especially the war. He seemed chronically demoralized by these two major events.

Becoming an American citizen in 1943 was a great occasion in his life. Did it mean both safety and acceptance? Our family's German citizenship had been stripped away by the Nazi government when we left the country so we were stateless. Dad had studied American history in great detail before his brief exam at the Federal Court House in Freehold.

After the ceremony, he took his friend, George Mathews, out for cocktails and steak—much to my amazement, since we could ill afford it. "You need to be older to understand the importance of this moment to your father," my mother told me afterwards.

Sally hated conflict and would go out of his way to avoid it. It took a lot to anger him and usually my mother, Rosi, won out easily, but he did show occasional flashes of temper, usually when Frank or I got into some serious mischief or Rosi pushed him a little to hard.

Mom dominated the family, partially in response to my father's emotional inability to rise above the crushing events that had brought us to America. Dad's clashes with our mother were always one-sided and invariably ended with his becoming disheartened and sitting alone in his car in tears.

After Sally recovered from the prostate surgery, he became gradually less self-reliant, depending more and more on Mom. And, as he became increasingly forgetful over the next few years, he also became irascible. His usually agreeable personality seemed to change. He became infuriated at the slightest provocation. Once he got an idea fixed in his mind, no matter how inappropriate, there was no dissuading him. Through it all, Mom managed to care for both of them.

The climax came a few years later and rather suddenly. They had moved to Milwaukee to be near Frank. In a fit of irrationality, Dad insisted on trying to shave with two safety blades—not one—in his razor. When this didn't work, he threw the razor into the toilet. At dinner that night he somehow fell from his chair and ended up on the floor under the table. He angrily refused any help and spent the night sleeping there. The next morning Mom called for help and the EMS took him to the hospital.

It was apparent that Dad could not go back home. His violent and aggressive behavior was making it impossible for the family to care for him. We found a nursing home near Frank in Milwaukee, where he and my mother could visit and supervise his care, which was difficult. He was furious with everyone and there was often no consoling him. He would yell that he was hungry, wolf down his food, and scream for more. On several occasions he bit his attendants. He needed to be tied into his chair during the day and into his bed at night to keep him from hurting himself. It was terrible for him and for all of us.

After a year, he finally slipped into a twilight state before dying. The ordeal was finally over. The father that Frank and I knew had been gone for a long time before he died.

As I look back, I wish I had known my dad better. His gracious manner had been his hallmark during the many years he worked in sales in Germany. He rarely talked about those years, but there must have been good times before the devastating political upheaval that cut off his career and changed the course of his life. I imagine my parents, in their thirties, rooted out of their comfortable way of life in Dresden by the Nazi threat. I have tried to picture their feelings during and after the flight with my infant brother and me to a whole new way of life in America. My father must have suffered terribly, trying to learn a new language in a strange country, not being able to make use of his considerable charm and business contacts and having to accept his undeserved fate.

Many years later, in the grip of Alzheimer's disease, with the feeling of helplessness it created in him, was his anger and his radical personality change due entirely to the effects of the illness? Or were his many frustrations—the poverty of his childhood, the fear and horror of two world wars, the destruction of his successful business career, and the domination of his overbearing wife—finally unleashed?

In the early days of Dad's illness, with our attention focused on him, Mom had seemed her usual self-reliant self. The illusion evaporated several days after we'd moved Dad to the nursing home.

Mom called me frantically, saying, "You've got to help me. I can't find my checkbook."

"Mom," I replied, "you don't have a checkbook. Don't you remember? My brother and I took over your finances two years ago."

She laughed, "Oh, of course. How silly of me. Sorry I bothered you."

Her laugh seemed a cover-up and I was suddenly struck with a new realization. I called my brother and told him the story. He was as incredulous as I. "Do you think Mom's getting Alzheimer's too?" he asked.

"I'm worried about it," I answered.

"Lud, we must have been so focused on Dad that we missed everything in Mom. We'll have to talk about what we're going to do," Frank said.

Mom and Dad were different in so many ways, but there was never any question that Mom was clearly in charge. She had strong, unbending opinions on most subjects. Many of these opinions revolved around the well-being of her family. Cold milk was bad for children. Wet feet caused the flu. Sitting on the chilly concrete back porch of our farmhouse caused kidney infections. There were plenty of additional strong judgments to go around: which relatives, acquaintances, religions, operas, and stores were good and which were bad. And she expected action and acquiescence from the family on all counts; no argument would sway her from her idea, even when she could show little proof. She was a woman who saw the world in only two colors—impenetrable black and dazzling white. Her relentless determination to stick with her beliefs made for constant battles in my growing-up years.

Dad kept his opinions to himself and, at least superficially, acquiesced to Mom's. At home, Mom ruled with an iron hand, but in public she always deferred to my father's smooth and charming style.

Rosi believed in discipline and she was a tough disciplinarian with Frank and me. At the same time, she made it abundantly clear that she loved us greatly. She went out of her way to do special things for each of us. More than once I expressed jealousies and she would always reassure me that I was "the best rooster in her basket." I have no doubt that Frank got the same speech. That she took great pride in our

accomplishments was always written indelibly in her beaming smile.

After Dad entered the nursing home, Rosi moved into a
nearby hotel that had been refurbished into apartments for senior citizens. She visited Dad almost every day, took walks
around the art museum, and went grocery shopping with her
granddaughter, Lily. As her forgetfulness got worse, she
became less domineering and opinionated. Her family would
frequently drop by to help her with her chores. When Lily
found her cooking straws instead of spaghetti for lunch, Rosi
could only laugh and marvel at her own mistake.

She would talk about how she had enjoyed riding horses on
the beach when she was a girl and swimming in the ocean when
she was older. She called her beach visits her "touch of heav-
en"—they were her most vivid and wonderful memories—and
now, more and more, these old recollections were edging her
memory of recent experiences out.

My concern about the effect Alzheimer's disease would
have on Mom—that she would become increasingly angry and
unmanageable, like Dad—proved to be wrong. In contrast to
my father, Mom gradually became gentler as her illness progressed. Dad had always been quiet, kind, and agreeable and,
to everyone's amazement, the illness turned his Dr. Jekyll
personality turned into Mr. Hyde.

My tough, assertive mother, on the other hand, became the
sweet, happy, charming woman I had never known. I often
thought this was the real Rosi. She had been the baby sister of
two older brothers and this must have been the way she was
when she was very young, before she had had to leave her
home—before her life changed.

After several years of holding her own, Mom's stay at the
Astor hotel came to a sudden end. An inappropriate question to

the hotel manager caused him to conclude that she was no longer competent. He'd have come to the same conclusion a year earlier had he known about her cooking drinking straws for pasta. It was clear the time had come to take action.

Frank and I had decided two years earlier that, when this moment came, I would take care of her in Morgantown. The next morning, Frank and Mom were on a plane.

Rosi sat quietly, looking out the window. She sang a little tune, softly, mostly to herself, "I'll never pass this way again, I'll never see this day again." My brother, Frank, sitting next to our mother, wasn't sure she really understood what was happening. He thought it was too complicated to try explaining to her and, yet, it seemed she knew anyway. She didn't seem upset and, as Mom had always been a forthright person, Frank decided she was okay with the move.

After picking her up at the airport, I realized, over the next several days, that she would need twenty-four-hour supervision. She was alert and active, but very forgetful and easily disoriented. The family decided a nursing home was the best option. Or, at least, some members of the family decided. One wasn't so sure.

Sundale Nursing Home was a large, old, two-story yellow brick building built in the early 1900s. It sat almost within the shadow of the big university hospital, a very convenient location for me, the caregiver.

My eighteen-year-old son, Rich, who had, rather unwillingly, helped move her into her room, confronted me that evening. "How could you do such an awful thing to Grandma? Did you really look at that place? It's full of old, decrepit people. That is no place for her to be." Rich loved his grandmother. He remembered her as caring and kind, her home always warm and welcoming to all the grandchildren.

I thought about it for a few minutes. "Okay," I said, "we'll bring her home and care for her here."

"Good," he said. "I wish you'd made that decision in the first place."

I knew he hadn't really pictured what we all were in for, so I laid it out for him. "You know she needs constant supervision day and night, every day of the year, and in one place—we can't move her around, the family will all have to come to our house in turns. So, before we bring her home, we have to do some planning. Since your sisters are away at college, we'll need to share the time. Your Mom and I can each work one eight-hour shift, but you need to work one as well. What part of the day would you like?"

There was a long pause. Rich was torn. He went to college in town, but he had a busy schedule. He finally answered, speaking very softly, "I don't have time to do that."

"Well," I answered, "the truth is that we don't really have time either. That's why the nursing home near us seemed the best option. You know, Rich, we're all here for your grandma, just as she always was for us. We're not deserting her, we're caring for her in the best way we can.

Rich seemed resigned, his initial anger dissipated, but I still had to deal with my own guilt. Mom had often told my brother and me that she never wanted to be placed in a nursing home. "It reminds me of the orphanage I grew up in as a child." Her father had placed her there after her mother died. "I do not want to end my life in an institution the way I began it." After making this flat statement, she would laugh and add, "But I know you boys—you'll do it the first chance you get. I will just have to stay strong and self-sufficient." The memory of her comment gave me no comfort at that moment.

Mom had been at Sundale for one day and, both to assuage Rich's unhappiness and to calm my own guilt, I suggested, "Let's go over for a visit together tomorrow and see how she's doing." Rich liked this idea.

Rosi was all excited to see us and share the news of the past twenty-four hours—or, at least, what she could remember of it. And what she could remember delighted her. "This is such a wonderful hotel. I can't imagine how you ever found it. My room faces the ocean; I can hear the surf all night long. You know how much I always loved the sea and your putting me so close to it was very thoughtful."

Rich looked perplexed. Morgantown is nowhere near the ocean. "I think it's the breeze rustling the leaves outside," I whispered. We both smiled and said nothing.

She continued, bubbling with delight, "And the food in the restaurant is so good—they must have a gourmet chef. I'm going to lunch right now. Come join me."

Lunch was a small hamburger and some wilted green string beans served on a plastic plate. It was typical nursing home food. During lunch another patient was yelling, refusing to eat. Rich looked concerned, but Mom simply laughed. "Just look at that old biddy! She's been disruptive at every meal since I've been here. It's best to ignore her."

Rich and I left after walking Rosi back to her room. "I'm amazed," Rich said. "She actually likes it here. She doesn't see the sorrow and tragedy of all these old people who have their best years behind them. To me it's really a sad place, but she doesn't seem to realize that."

I nodded my head. Of course Rich was right. "You know, I think there's an important lesson here for both of us. The only thing that matters is what your grandmother sees and that she's happy, not what we see. Her Alzheimer's disease alters her view of the world—fortunately for everyone."

During the last few years of my mother's life, when she was lying in a vegetative state in the nursing home, slowly dying of Alzheimer's disease, I would visit her as her physician, not just her son, and attend to any of her special needs and rewrite her nursing and medicine orders.

Each time I would visit her in her room, always saying, "Hi, Mom," as I entered, I had a momentary hope that this time, this one last time, she would look at me, smile, and say "Hi, son, haven't seen you in a while…" The experienced neurologist in me knew the expectation was in vain but this could not override the short-lived hopes and wishes of the son.

The rest of the family had stopped visiting Grandma during the last two years of her life as she became more and more withdrawn, unable to recognize anyone, lying quietly curled up in bed. It was difficult for everyone. I didn't encourage them to visit. I felt they each had their own happy memories of their Grandma as a dynamic and caring woman and seeing her in her current state would fill them with enormous and unnecessary sadness.

But, a few weeks before she quietly died, my son, Rich, decided he needed to see his grandmother one last time. "Are you sure you want to?" I asked him. "Why not remember her as she was—the woman who helped raise you, loved you, cared for you, and played with you, the grandmother who always made your favorite foods for you. That woman you loved so dearly has already left us. Let it be."

"No, I need to see her one last time. I have to do this for myself."

We entered her room. Rich talked to her quietly but she just stared at the ceiling, comfortably resting but disconnected from the world. There was no response, no recognition, not even an acknowledgement that anyone was in the room with her. Her body was still there, her heart beating and her lungs breathing, but the woman we had known and loved had already left.

"You were right," he said wistfully, after a few minutes. "This is not how I want to remember my grandmother. I wish I hadn't come."

I suddenly thought of the last time I'd seen my father. It had been years earlier. He was tied into an old easy chair with a rolled up bed sheet, shouting while he attacked an apple I'd given him. He voraciously devoured it, all of it—the apple, the stem, the core, in three gulps, then screamed for another. And yet, I don't remember that as happening to my father. I remember him as the quiet, gentle man I knew and loved all my life—a far cry from the angry man he became for a while. The angry man just wasn't him to me, or to any of us.

I looked at my son, a young man in his mid-twenties, gentle, and handsome, worriedly looking at his grandmother who was totally changed from the woman he had known, and approaching her death. I felt I had to put it in a better perspective for him. He needed to choose the person he would remember, as we all have chosen.

"You know," I said, "there was a lot of turmoil and worry in Grandma's life, what with all the fears of escaping from Nazi Germany and having to make her way in a strange new country with two young sons. She was strong and resilient and a wonderful role model for all of us. You three grandkids remember her in her later years, after she had mellowed, as your loving Grandma, not as you've seen her today. Watching her gradually drift away, as the Alzheimer's disease devastated her brain ever so slowly, has been hard for all of us.

During the ten years she spent in the nursing home, her perception of her world was one of child-like fascination, full of pleasant surprises and happiness—all the anxieties of the past gone. These last years, when she was completely unresponsive, must have been like a deep, comfortable sleep to her—a gentle way out of a long and productive life. Think of it in those terms and let's celebrate her having been with us."

Beyond 168 Street

I STOOD, with two other freshman medical students, at the corner of 168th Street and Fort Washington Avenue in New York City, waiting nervously for the light to change. We had spent a frustrating morning getting supplies and trying to find lecture halls in a large, confusing building. Now, after having waited with some irritation in line for lunch at a busy deli, we were hurrying back, worried we might be late. An unseasonably cold wind off the Hudson made us draw our light coats tightly around us. It was not a day to stand still.

A complex of tall gray vintage 1900 buildings, Columbia University's College of Physicians and Surgeons, filled one side of the street with an imposing, four-story armory opposite. The drabness of this part of Manhattan was broken up by glimpses of the Hudson River and the George Washington Bridge far below. The area has always been a sort of "college town"— its own island in the city—with professors in long white coats and students in shorter white jackets moving quickly, often talking excitedly in groups, rushing from class to class and building to building. The subway stop at the Broadway corner is always filled with people running up the steps from rides or down the steps to get them. People move quickly in that part of town.

As I looked up the street, I suddenly drew a deep breath as I saw a ragged line of older people moving directly toward us.

In marked contrast to everyone else, and clearly purposeful, they walked at a very slow, measured pace—not together, exactly, but looking so much alike they seemed together.

"Hey, John," I nudged one of my new buddies, "look at those people."

We gaped at them, all conventions of politeness gone. They walked stooped over in a labored, mechanical fashion; taking small, slow, shuffling steps—like toy soldiers winding down. They didn't swing their arms at all, just held them rigidly bent at the elbow. Some had trembling hands. As they came closer, we began to see that their faces were completely spiritless and immobile. They had no expression or animation at all and they just kept staring fixedly straight ahead. These people didn't seem to know one another, but it was clear they were all going somewhere very slowly, and with great determination, in spite of the cold. The effect was powerful and we were mesmerized, transfixed—three frozen statues, awed by what we were seeing, completely forgetting our haste, as the light changed several times. They just kept on coming, one after another, after another, after another, after another—more than fifteen in all—shuffling slowly up out of the subway at the other end of the block, advancing directly toward us in a steady stream.

"Wow, they're all look-alikes," John whispered. "It's as if they're aliens from another planet."

"If I didn't know better, I'd think we were in the middle of a science fiction movie," David said. The comfortable, known world had suddenly become surreal.

An older man in a long white coat had been standing to one side, watching the scene with some amusement as we stood rooted, entranced. Finally he came over and chuckling, said to us, "From your perplexed and astonished expressions and your clean, freshly starched white coats, I'd say you are new freshman medical students. As you will soon learn, what you are seeing here—so many people looking like a series of reproductions—should tell you something. These people all have the same illness. You can diagnose it just by looking at them. They're all coming here for treatment. Today is Parkinson's clinic day at the Neurologic Institute."

The world tipped back to normal—to something we could deal with. We understood. We made the connection. The spell was broken. We glanced at our watches and hurried on to class.

At that time I had no clue as to the mysteries of this debilitating disease. Like a boy using a magnet for the first time, this experiment of nature—called Parkinson's disease—filled me with wonder and amazement and was the first step in directing my career into the world of neurons, axons, and synaptic connections.

With Parkinson's disease, what you see is what it is. The symptoms are easy to spot. The first clue is a mild, involuntary shaking, a tremor starting in one hand. Most tremors occur when muscles are active—when using a fork or drinking from a cup—but the Parkinson's tremor is unique; it happens when the patient is resting and relaxed. One of my patients, a carpenter who had developed a new onset Parkinsonian tremor in his right hand, declined to take any medication for two years. "It sure is present when I watch television or when I'm here talking with you, but put a hammer or a saw in my hand and there's not so much as a twitch," he said.

The next symptom is stiffness in the arms and legs. The patient walks with a shuffling, mechanical gait and the face loses expression, like a painted mask. The symptoms intensify as years go by.

No tests, including MRI scans, can be made to confirm the Parkinson's diagnosis. It's all there in the portrait the patient presents and making the connection depends on the doctor's experience. All portray the same classical findings of this disabling disease to one degree or another.

A DECADE LATER I was confronted by a personable, comely young patient with all the symptoms and signs of this devastating disease. Dorothy Harris was still in the early stages but what was she doing with a disorder that nearly always afflicted the elderly? When I took her history, the story got even worse—the typical Parkinson tremor had begun in her left hand when she was barely out of her teenage years, ten years before.

One percent of the population over sixty five is afflicted with Parkinson's disease—very few under sixty five develop it. We may not know the exact trigger that gets Parkinson's going, but we do know what happens inside the brain. A small clump of darkly pigmented neurons deep in the brain—called the "substantia nigra"—begin to degenerate. In the normally functioning brain, dopamine, which is one of the all-important chemical neurotransmitters, is released by the nerve fibers arising from the cells of the substantia nigra. The degenerating cells slowly release less dopamine than needed and it is the waning amount of this transmitter that results in Parkinson's disease. These nerve fibers are part of the complex pathways that carry the intricate messages from the brain that initiate and fine tune motor activity in the muscles of the body.

But why does the substantia nigra degenerate? Genetic abnormalities are probably the biggest culprits. We know the gene abnormality in some of the familial cases but not in the majority of patients. Viruses, environmental toxins, and trauma have also been proposed, but their role is probably small if they play any part at all. So the cause remains, at least partially, a mystery—but the treatments are not.

When I first saw Dorothy Harris in 1967 at West Virginia University Hospital, research into this ailment was just beginning to explain some of the questions. We knew about the degenerating substantia nigra but nothing about dopamine or any useful therapies. Dorothy had all the typical features usually seen in patients over sixty. The symptoms had started with the typical resting tremor of Parkinson's disease in her left hand seven years earlier and, finally, her baffled doctors had sent her to see my colleagues and me. The somber poker-faced feature, the stooped posture, mechanical gait, and slowness of movement—the characteristic picture of Parkinson's disease—were all there. The changes in her appearance were all mild and, for the moment not disabling. Her age was the only unique feature.

I took blood samples, testing for other related diagnostic possibilities and, after they all came back negative, I sat down with Dorothy and her husband, Salty. They were holding hands, two young people very much in love, devoted to each other. I felt very uncomfortable with the message I was about to deliver; there was no easy way to say it.

"Dorothy, we think you have Parkinson's disease even though you're awfully young, but the tests for other illnesses that look similar have come back normal. We've never seen this disease begin at such a young age. We do have some medicines that may help."

Both Dorothy and Salty looked perplexed. I could see they'd never heard of Parkinson's. I quickly realized I was about to lead them into troubling and uncharted waters. I gave them a simple outline, explained that this was a chronic disease, and told them there was no cure. "The symptoms will slowly get worse over many years, but we'll do the best we can do to help you." This was the part I had dreaded talking about; I knew we had little ammunition in our therapeutic arsenal.

Still, I wanted to put the best face on it I could. Dorothy and Salty were so full of hope and faith. I found it impossible to tell them that her future would be filled with increasing disability—that the medicines available to us were of little value in stemming the inexorable worsening of the illness. She would be an invalid in another decade.

Dorothy's reaction was positive and she was immediately determined to do battle. "I'm going to fight this, and I know Salty will help me." Salty, still holding her hand, nodded his head, yes. "We've got a little girl and a new baby boy and they need us, especially the baby. He's just been diagnosed with Down's syndrome."

Two serious unrelated disorders, I thought. This young couple with two young children and a slowly debilitating and mostly untreatable disease—they would have their hands full. I remembered the ragged line of patients shuffling slowly down 168th Street—how long before she would be one of them?

FORTY YEARS LATER, as I looked out my office window, a car pulled slowly into the large parking lot in front of the Physician's Office Center. A middle aged woman got out of the driver's side and brought a wheel chair out of the back. Dorothy Harris climbed out from the other side and walked slowly, her steps unsure, over to the chair where the younger woman waited.

I watched and was surprised to see it was Dorothy who was riding in a wheel chair and again felt disappointed that Salty wasn't there. Several months ago she'd have walked from the car. Still, I couldn't have imagined this scene 40 years ago. Fifty years earlier she'd have been an invalid—if she had survived at all. I could imagine the conversation Dorothy was having with her daughter, Sharee.

"You know, Sharee, I could have walked over by myself a few months ago," Dorothy said, sitting up straight in the chair.

"Nothing seems to have gone well since Dad got so sick with his cancer,"

"I don't know how I'll get along without him," Dorothy said. Her warm tears mixed with the light cold drizzle of the gray December day.

"Joe and I'll be there to help," Sharee responded.

"Joe is such a good boy," Dorothy said. "It's hard to believe when he was little, Salty and I thought we'd have to look after him the rest of his life. Instead, he's been looking after us."

If there is any neurological disorder that exemplifies the advances made by modern medicine during the past half century, it is Parkinson's disease. James Parkinson first described the disease in *An Essay on the Shaking Palsy* in 1817.

For the next 150 years nothing happened to change the course of this crippling illness. The underlying biochemical change in the brain—the missing dopamine—was identified in the 1950s due largely to the work of the Nobel Prize winning Swedish scientist, Arvid Carlsson.

The first major breakthrough came in 1969 when levodopa, the precursor to dopamine, became available as an experimental drug to treat Parkinson's disease. Levodopa was taken up by the surviving cells of the substantia nigra which fueled their ability to release extra amounts of dopamine. Research articles claimed it to be effective in treating Parkinson's.

Patients afflicted with this incapacitating disease had waited with intense anticipation for years while their symptoms worsened—the promise of levodopa had received extensive publicity.

Others, like Dorothy, were newcomers to the waiting list. The longer the wai—the more passionate the patients' pleas to be included in the clinical trials.

We began treating a small cadre of patients. Dorothy was high on the list of the patients we placed on this experimental drug but she was not among the first.

One of the initial patients was the former attorney general of an adjacent state. As I stood in the clinic doorway watching him walk, I could tell that he was severely affected. He was stooped over and moved slowly, taking small, uncertain steps with his arms flexed and immobile. The tremor of his arms made his whole body shake.

As we sat down to talk, his face was expressionless and his soft voice, barely audible. "I'm so glad you agreed to see me. I've been desperate to enroll in this study. I couldn't get in at two other university centers and I've waited for years as my symptoms kept getting worse. I don't know what I would have done if you had rejected me too."

As I watched this slim, tall man with silver white hair, bent forward as if he carried the woes of the world on his shoulders, I could easily imagine that he had once been very handsome. He seemed an ideal candidate so we decided to enroll him even though he was in his 80s. We gave him a supply of levodopa, with instructions to begin at a very low dose and gradually increase it.

I saw him again some weeks later. He seemed transformed, walking down the hall almost normally. There was still a slight stoop to his posture, but his steps were sure and firm and he swung his arms freely. The tremor in his hands was almost gone.

I was impressed and delighted. Not so my patient. He was able to smile now if he wished, but his expression was flat and serious when I exclaimed, "What a great response. You're doing wonderfully, you're almost normal again. We couldn't ask for more."

He sighed, "Yes, I am better in some ways, but I had expected more. While I waited for this drug over the last few agonizing years, I had such high hopes for it. It has helped, but I think I expected to find my fountain of youth in it. Now I realize I'm still an old man. It hasn't changed that."

He marched off down the hall and all I could think was, too bad he can't see how lucky he is. Not many years ago, without this medicine, he would soon have been in a wheelchair.

His daughter called me one week later in tears. Without warning, and without leaving a note, Thomas had climbed on the roof of his house and jumped off, fracturing his neck. He died several hours later.

I was aghast. I was also concerned about the implications—that it might be a complication of using the drug. Still, one week later I had Dorothy begin using levo-dopa. As she gradually increased the dosage, her response became increasingly dramatic to the point where she was able to lead a totally unencumbered, normal life. It was hard to tell she had Parkinson's disease at all. She and Salty couldn't have been happier.

The suicide issue stayed with us. Of the first ten patients we had placed on the drug, levodopa, two others also committed suicide. The wife of a professor had drowned herself in a local pond and a retired trial lawyer had shot himself with his handgun. Both had had excellent responses, as far as we were concerned. Their symptoms, which had been extreme and intractable, were almost gone. It was reminiscent of the former attorney general.

We thought suicide might be a side-effect but it turned out not to be the case. After this initial flurry, it has not happened again. In retrospect, it seemed due to the prolonged waiting periods. I have come to believe it was the great expectations that led to the suicides. Patients saw themselves as not aging, only ill. The eighty-year-old who had developed the illness in his sixties thought he was still sixty—just unwell. He didn't count on the ageing process that had continued through the years as he waited for the medicine. His connection with reality was thin and his level of anticipation for a return to youth was so high that this new medicine, no matter how effective, could never completely fulfill his unrealistic hopes and dreams. And, by unchaining him from the grasp of his disease, we'd made it possible for him to climb up on the roof.

One year after we began using levodopa experimentally, it was approved by the FDA and represented a major breakthrough in the treatment of Parkinson's disease. Several years later, levodopa was combined with carbidopa, another new drug that enhances the absorption of levodopa from the gastrointestinal tract into the brain. This combination has been used with amazing results for more than thirty years. It still remains the most effective medication for this disorder.

The response to levodopa explained the mystery of the wheel chair-ridden old man I remembered from medical school. His sudden explosive action in a moment of intense anger had haunted me. I now knew that levodopa is metabolized to dopamine in the brain. Some of the dopamine is then converted further to adrenaline. The powerful emotional event must have prompted the sudden increase in the production of both dopamine and adrenaline. The increase in available dopamine allowed the anchored elderly Prometheus to momentarily break his chains. Sad that the effect didn't last.

Dorothy's wonderful response continued for many years. During this time, Dorothy's children grew up, she was an active member of her community, and it appeared that her recovery—

while not a cure—would be a lasting one, but one day she began to notice changes.

"Something unusual has begun happening," Dorothy told me during one of her routine visits. "There are times during every day that the medicine doesn't seem to work so well."

"Don't forget to tell him, honey, that when it does work it sometimes works too good," Salty added.

"Yes, I can get real fidgety. My arms and legs want to move on their own."

I nodded my head. We were just beginning to learn that this great medicine came with a flaw. It had provided an on switch for Dorothy, but now a hidden off switch was making its appearance. The surviving cells of the substantia nigra still produced dopamine and they were having difficulty regulating the output. There were times when too much dopamine was being released and that caused abnormal, involuntary, purposeless movements of the arms, legs, and head. These out-of-control tics and gyrations became known as dopa dyskinesia and the impression they gave was of a mind and body that were out of sync. At other times there was too little dopamine, and this resulted in off periods. Dorothy and other patients, especially those with the most positive, dramatic responses had begun to notice fluctuations after years of using the new medications. The condition was ultimately referred to as the on-off effect of the drug.

Dorothy's off periods gradually became more frequent and prolonged. They became so severe she could hardly move for many hours each day.

"When I'm on," she told me, "I rush around doing my housework and cooking. I bake, and clean, and do the laundry. But when I'm off, I can't do anything. I shake violently and can hardly move. I just sit on the couch and watch television.

Sometimes when I'm shopping and feeling just fine all of a sudden it turns into a disaster—I feel like someone has just turned out the lights. I never know when the switch will turn off and I'll become a frozen statue, clinging to my grocery cart, hoping and praying for help."

The next years were trying as the off periods lasted longer and longer. For a while, beginning in 1998, apomorphine, a new drug that stimulates dopamine receptor sites directly, helped to shorten the time Dorothy spent off. Salty would inject the medicine whenever an off episode began and Dorothy would be back on again. The apomorphine injections worked well for a while until the overshoots during her on periods became more violent. The involuntary tics and gyrations of her body were as incapacitating as the Parkinson's disease. Dorothy managed to cope during these difficult times only through Salty's devotion and loyalty.

It was finally time to consider a surgical option. Placing electrical stimulators into both subthalamic nuclei—a part of the complex brain motor control system—should result in striking improvement of Parkinson's disease and allow for major reductions in the medications while side effects should be minimal. The patients showing the most striking improvement were those, like Dorothy, in whom the response to carbidopa-levodopa and apomorphine was excellent. The on-off episodes should disappear as well as the violent movements of the on episodes.

Salty, who was ill himself at this late date in their lives, still wanted all the details—how the surgeon would find the subthalamic nucleus deep in the brain, the method for implanting the electrodes into the chest wall, and how would he know when the batteries needed changing? Dorothy listened patiently but she had made up her mind—she was going to do it.

The process was complicated but the stimulator wires were successfully implanted. On the next few visits to the clinic the implanted stimulators were carefully adjusted with a remote computer. Dorothy's dose of carbidopa-levodopa was halved and most of her side effects disappeared.

"I think I'm as good now as I was forty years ago when I first started L-dopa," she said on her next visit. I thought so, too. And for the next few months that's how it remained.

DOROTHY ARRIVED UPSTAIRS for her appointment. After watching out the window, I was waiting for her. She stepped hesitantly into the exam room, leaving the wheelchair in the hallway. I shook my head with concern. "You're not doing as well as you were," I said. As Dorothy walked I'd seen her shuffling gait. I knew Salty had died a few weeks before, and I hoped that this worsening was due to her grief and that some adjustments would make her more mobile. But I also knew that age was beginning to make a contribution and, as my former attorney general patient tragically discovered, there was no treatment for that.

"Salty was so sick. It's been hard." Dorothy was sobbing softly. "I really miss him. We were together all our lives."

All your lives, I thought as I looked at her, and my life, as well—more than forty years of my life in medicine treating Parkinson's disease in Dorothy and in other patients. From seeing the terribly incapacitated but terribly determined patients when I was a medical student, through the early years, when little was available in the way of treatments, I remember the helpless feeling I had when yet another patient showed the unmistakable signs.

But there was no one like Dorothy. She and Salty made a life together that had many happy times in spite of Dorothy's infirmities. She saw her life clearly and rejoiced in each new medical advance as it became available. In fact, reviewing her story is reviewing the history of a major success in modern medical treatments.

But life does not go on forever. Her companion is gone and how can I comfort her now? What can I say at this late hour? I can do little to alter the course of her Parkinson's disease. I can only share in her good memories, express my admiration for her, and salute her indomitable courage throughout her life.

About the Author
Lud Gutmann, MD

LUD GUTMANN cares for his patients and teaches medical students and residents at the West Virginia University Health Sciences Center where he holds the Hazel Ruby McQuain Chair as Professor of Neurology. His career in medicine began after his graduation from Princeton University in 1955, when he attended medical school at Columbia University's College of Physicians and Surgeons. This was followed by a neurology residency at the University of Wisconsin, and a clinical neurophysiology fellowship at the Mayo Clinic.

He helped establish Neurology at West Virginia University and chaired the department for 28 years. He has been a vice-president and a director of the American Board of Psychiatry and Neurology and has served on the editorial boards of several neurological journals. In 1993, he received an honorary doctorate degree from the University of Mainz, in Mainz, Germany. His research has focused on diseases of muscles and nerves and he has published more than 160 scientific articles in peer-reviewed journals.

Treating patients has always been his central focus and telling stories which feature them has grown out of this work. His writing has appeared in various magazines and professional journals. He lives in Morgantown, West Virginia with his wife, Mary, his devoted companion and editor.